LOST SCROLLS

Of

NEWGRANGE

The
LOST SCROLLS
Of
NEWGRANGE

TOM RICHARDS

POOLBEG

Published in 1994 by
Poolbeg,
A division of Poolbeg Enterprises Ltd,
Knocksedan House,
123 Baldoyle Industrial Estate,
Dublin 13, Ireland

© Tom Richards 1994

A catalogue record for this book is available from the British Library.

ISBN 1 85371 299 X

Cover illustration by Jane Doran
Cover design by Poolbeg Group Services Ltd
Set by Poolbeg Group Services Ltd in Palatino 9.5/12.5
Printed by The Guernsey Press Company Ltd,
Vale, Guernsey, Channel Islands.

To Bernadette and the children. Your love is the anchor of my wind-swept life. To that love, I dedicate this first novel.

Prologue

The early morning sun cast its shadow over the far valley wall as the old man made his way uncomfortably through the hedgerow. It was early; too early for the guards to be out. He knew about this, of course. He had studied their movements for many weeks and was certain that he would be alone. This was essential. He needed absolute solitude for this part of the study. It would not do at all to have the local neighbours see his investigations. And if the local militia chose to show up – God forbid! – that would be the end of months of work.

He squatted in the wet grass at the edge of the clearing. With great care, he smoothed the moustache which framed his mouth, and surveyed the area. No one in sight. Slowly, he rose. As he did so, the great sun made its triumphant arrival, blinding him for a moment. Then his vision cleared and in front of him stood the dark outlines of the great megalithic monument at Newgrange.

He stood for a moment, looking at it again, taking in the great proportions, the tonnes of rock and earth which had stood for over five thousand years. It never ceased to fascinate him, and he knew that men greater than he had pondered on its secrets, trying to determine its ultimate function. He smiled briefly as he remembered some of the many hypotheses which he had read.

Located north of Dublin, the capital of Ireland, the Newgrange monument meant many things to many people. Its huge bulk, lying like some alien craft, had been subjected to

1

intense scrutiny by some of the world's most noted archaeologists. Many thought the mound to be a place of worship. Some thought it was a cemetery, a place where the great kings of old were buried. Others posited the monument to be an astronomical observatory; a huge stone observation post from which megalithic man gained insight into the changes of the stars and seasons. But these were only the intelligent guesses of men who had spent lifetimes trying to unlock the monument's ancient puzzle. These men knew, of course, that the answers died with the people who had built the structure. Today's scientists would never know the real purpose of Newgrange . . .

The old man shook his head slightly, remembering all the men who had tried to solve the puzzle and failed. He looked again at the huge structure. Cautiously, he made his way up the grassy slope toward the mound and to the secret opening he had discovered. He put out his hand. The great stone shifted a little, then swung open to reveal the ancient, dust-laden stairs which led down into the bowels of the earth. He stood for a moment, deep in thought. The sun, streaming over the horizon, struck the side of the great mound with its glorious light, revealing the design which had been carved deeply into the huge stone. Absently, he touched it, running his fingers along grooves which had been chiselled there so many thousands of years ago. The smile on his ruddy face deepened. He was suddenly certain: this day, the ancient puzzle would reveal its closely guarded secrets. He shone a torch down into the chasm. Then he went inside and the giant stone closed behind him, leaving the sun to warm the great mound which men call Newgrange.

PART ONE

The Cataclysm

1

In the fifth millennium BC, five thousand years before the birth of Christ, a proud and prosperous people evolved into a civilisation which would not be matched for another seven thousand years. Founded on a continent which no longer exists, located off the western seaboard of what is now modern-day Europe, these people created a culture which aspired to optimise the talents of the individual within their society.

War did not exist. Hunger was only a distant memory. Care of the sick and old was taken for granted. This people wanted nothing more than to live in peace and took from the world only that which they believed necessary. Their lives were worthy. They sought wisdom from the land and ocean around them. They studied many things and used their knowledge to serve the people in the world around them.

For almost two thousand years, these people devised tools and implements. Great cities were built, sprawling metropolises which sheltered them from the elements, and upon which they carved their unique signature. They created art, and used painting and sculpture to record the most important aspects of their lives.

They learned to write, to communicate their thoughts and decisions on a form of paper which was so fine that they protected it between sheets of glass. They founded industries, fished the seas, developed land and sea transport and looked at the next frontier – conquering the skies.

Of all their people and specialists – the farmers, factory

workers, industrialists and administrators – it was the scientists and engineers who looked beyond the horizons and sought to learn the secrets of space and time.

In this society there lived a man named Psorsis. Through hard work, determination and innate intellect, he had advanced to the position of head mathematician and now, in his middle years, he had been assigned to the study of the planets and stars, to learn the intricacies of their motion and the nature of their matter. To Psorsis, the study of these objects was a vocation. Day after day, he studied the works of scholars who had preceded him. As a youth, he had pored over equations, studying the effect each celestial body had upon the others. As he studied, he realised that his predecessors had barely scratched the surface of such knowledge. And with his usual determination, Psorsis began to delve deeper into the mysteries of the universe.

As Psorsis worked through the old writings, he developed his own theories of motion and time but these seemed to pose yet more questions. He plodded on, undaunted. His calculations and analyses ran into many volumes and his teachers and colleagues could only admire him, convinced that one day he would find the meaning of life itself.

In his fiftieth year, Psorsis grew tired of mere figures. At night, he gazed up at the heavens, at the myriad bodies floating through a dark sea, and marvelled at their beauty. Not content to observe them with the naked eye, Psorsis perfected a series of glass lenses which he encased in a tube of carefully finished wood. With his new instrument, Psorsis could view the planets and stars more clearly, and he realised that his study into their nature had only begun. From then on, he spent many hours observing the stars and what lay beyond them. It was Psorsis who noted the faint rings around the planet which burned so brightly on a winter's night. It was Psorsis who dared to look into the face of the sun, using a series of filters to protect his eyes from blindness. It was Psorsis who accurately mapped the face of the moon, who observed its craters and mountains, and who dared to think that man might set foot upon that empty, yet strangely welcoming globe.

And finally, it was Psorsis who one day noted the faint light in the eastern sky, and who charted its path nightly. It was he, through his series of glass lenses, who noted the strange shape of it, like the hairs of a horse's tail at full gallop. And, through a series of mathematical calculations, it was he who was able to predict that this faint light, growing in intensity as it approached, would one day hurtle towards the planet which was his birthplace.

Psorsis named the new star Borgnoff – The Destroyer. Now that he realised the ultimate destination of the new star in the east, he sat for many hours, considering his next course of action. For he knew that he must tell the elders of the community. And he knew that when he told them, they would not believe him.

For Psorsis knew that as the star grew brighter, so did it spell disaster. Knowing this, he remained silent and spent the next three months assembling his life's works, which were considerable. Much of his accumulated knowledge he would not have time to put to use. But he knew that his studies could provide humankind with untold wealth. Psorsis meant to preserve it.

With great care, the scholar recorded all his calculations, inscribing them on paper as a series of mathematical equations. Then, when he had finished, he fused them into protective plates of glass. In turn, these plates were placed into a glass box and the top was sealed to protect the wealth within. Finally, the box was placed into a wooden carrying vessel which protected the contents even further. When he had finished, Psorsis rested easier. He knew that if he could convince the elders, the heart of his learning might yet survive. And with it, his culture.

When he was ready, Psorsis told the elders of their destiny. At first, they did not believe him, even when he showed them Borgnoff – a small fiery star shining in the east. But as the months passed, the star grew until it became a huge smear of light, an evil dragon descending on them, ready to devour them. Finally, the elders were convinced. "Do you see?" said Psorsis. "My predictions are coming true as my equations said they would."

The elders were frightened. "What are we to do?" they asked.

"Many of us will surely die. But if you take action now, you can save our culture from extinction."

"How, Psorsis, how?" they begged him.

He waited until they grew quiet, then told the elders of his plans. "You can do nothing for the many, but you can save the few. Gather our best people and send them from here, away to the east. Borgnoff will fall here, on our continent. Yet, with luck, these few shall escape its wrath, and our culture, our society, may yet survive."

The elders agreed to his plan. They assembled five thousand of their best people. Women and men. Artisans, craftsmen, engineers, scientists, mathematicians. Psorsis, too old now to travel, or to endure hardship, elected to stay in his doomed and beloved city. He sent Midreas, his son, in his place, and Dorea, his daughter, to accompany him. On the day of their leaving, Psorsis placed the great wooden vessel that contained his life's work into the care of his son and daughter.

"In this ark rests knowledge greater than men have yet known, and beyond their understanding. In here, my children, I give you the keys to the universe. I give you a means to explore places and times which today seem unreachable. Here are my scrolls. Take them with you and guard them well. Study hard and you will learn from them. You will have to study harder still to apply what you have learned. But I believe that you can take our people and lead them to a new place; a place of beauty where you may yet raise your own sons and daughters, far away from the doom which Borgnoff now brings to us. Go to the east. But never forget your birthplace. This planet is your womb, and you have a responsibility to protect it from disasters still to come. I beg you to remember this always."

Psorsis hugged them both in blessing. And then they left,

joining their people. The chosen ones streamed out through the city gates, fleeing for their lives, with the scrolls which Psorsis had given to them held closely to their breasts.

In the two hundred and forty-second year of the third millennium, the comet which the people called Borgnoff descended to Earth. Plunging quickly through its upper atmosphere, it plunged to the ground. When it hit, the comet and land mass blended for a moment, and then rose up in a great ball of blinding light, sending out massive shock waves. The energy of the blast levelled everything in its path for hundreds of square kilometres. Whole cities melted in the intense heat. The land mass, now unstable, fissured and split as earthquakes rocked its expanse. Tidal waves flooded what had been a monument to civilisation only hours before.

From a distance, the son and daughter of Psorsis saw the great light and felt the earth tremble. They knew then that their father and all who had been left behind were gone from them forever. Gently, Midreas touched the vessel which his father had given to his care. Then, he turned his back on the destruction and set out to seek a new land.

Such was the end of the continent of Atlantis. Such was the exodus of her people.

9

2

Midreas led the survivors of Atlantis away from the shattered remains of their country. Earthquakes rocked the land daily, and with each tremor the travellers fell to their knees, praying to their gods that they would live. Great fissures ripped the very rocks in two, and once Midreas watched helplessly as the ground opened beneath twelve of his people, watched as they fell into a black void that seemed never-ending.

He assumed leadership of his people, and as leader, divided the five thousand into five tribes, each led by a tribal lord. Midreas assumed leadership of one of the tribes. To each of the lords, Midreas stated, "We are the caretakers of the greatness that was Atlantis. The people whom you now lead are in your care. In their minds, and in their loins, lies that which will enable our people and culture to survive beyond this day. On you rests the responsibility to care for your people, to see that they survive. Only through our survival will Atlantis endure."

The leaders of the tribes took charge of their people, and the few supplies that they carried were assigned to Dorea for care and distribution. They appointed a group of gatherers, to supplement their supplies by hunting for animals and looking for edible vegetation. Engineers were charged with building shelters when the people stopped to rest.

Midreas kept charge of the scrolls of Psorsis, never leaving them out of his sight for long. He remembered his father's words, that the scrolls held the knowledge of the nature of the universe, and he sometimes let his mind consider the future, when his people would be able to study his father's work and when they could use this to rebuild their great civilisation.

The group trudged wearily eastward, away from the broken continent, seeking a new land upon which they could settle. Each morning, Midreas greeted the rising sun, praying that this day would find them in their new lands. His prayers went unanswered.

Late one evening, as rough shelters were being erected to house the people for the night, Midreas's sister, Dorea, came to him. For the past three months, she had been in charge of the food and the cooking, organising the women of each tribe to prepare the food which the gatherers found and rationing their remaining provisions.

She found Midreas standing on a small hill, glumly looking out at the shattered lands that surrounded him. Wearily, she walked up the hill to join him.

"The land is still no good, Midreas," she said.

"It is not," he agreed.

Together they surveyed the wreckage that surrounded them. Everywhere, the land was upturned from earthquakes and aftershocks. It had rained each day for the previous month, large muddy drops laden with the earthen mixture thrown up by the comet. His people knew that these drops also held the ashes of their relatives and loved ones.

Great lakes had formed in the depressions caused by the earthquakes. Trees lay uprooted, their leaves turned a dusty grey. In the distance they could see a new range of mountains thrown up by the great upheavals that still shook the earth daily.

Midreas turned to his sister. "This land is uninhabitable. We must keep searching."

"Our people are tired. Food is running short."

He took her by the shoulder. "We must walk to survive."

In the seventh month of their journey, Midreas realised that he must divide up his people if they were to survive. At the next sunrise he called the other four leaders to him. Once proud men, now exhausted by their efforts to protect their people, they came to hear him speak. Midreas addressed them, Dorea standing at his side.

"For months we have journeyed eastward together in the hope of finding a place to make a new beginning. We have managed to survive on the provisions which we brought with us and the food which has been found by the gatherers."

He looked at them earnestly. "Now we are facing a dilemma. Dorea has told me that our provisions are almost exhausted."

A murmur of fear rose from the small group. Midreas waited until it died down, then continued. "The land remains poor, is even poorer than when we started. I have talked to our farmers and they say it is due to the rain. The land is sodden. Vegetation is spoiling, and any animal life that survived has fled. It is no longer possible to feed five thousand people from the land."

Midreas paused, letting his words take hold. "So," he continued, "I have made a decision. On this day, we shall divide our five thousand. Each of you will take your group and travel alone. We shall all continue east, but we shall do so in different directions. Two of the groups shall head north-east, two groups south-east. I with the scrolls of Psorsis shall lead the last group, directly east, in the direction of the sun as it rises. In this way, we shall have a better chance of survival. Go, each of you now, and tell your people."

And so it happened that Midreas stood and watched as four thousand of his people left to seek their own land. Dorea stood beside him as they departed and he said to her, "Now, Dorea, the people of Atlantis shall not only survive but shall populate the world. Come, let us continue our journey."

With his thousand people behind him, and with the sacred scrolls, he set out once again.

For two years more, Midreas walked with his people. During this time, many of them died, some from exhaustion, some of starvation. Some were left behind, injured, doomed never to walk again.

During that time the land they journeyed through did not

show any improvement. It remained barren and Midreas began to think that the whole world had been laid waste by the comet.

In the twenty-fifth month of their journey, they came to a great expanse of water. On the far side they could see land and Midreas announced that they must build boats if they were to continue. For five weeks, his people scavenged the land for wood. His carpenters shaped the wood into small boats, each of which could contain a score of people. At the end of the fifth week, they were ready for their voyage and launched the boats into the sea.

With the scrolls lashed firmly to his boat, Midreas and his people set out for the opposite shore. During their voyage, they passed many islands, and Midreas could see that they were new, formed as a result of the earth's convulsions. He did not look back. Midreas knew that the land they had left behind was doomed; that the entire continent would soon sink into the sea.

At the end of the second day, they came to shore. All of his people had survived the crossing.

When Midreas stepped on to the land, he knew that he had at last found a new home for his people. Here, the earth had not been subjected to turmoil. Fresh green grass grew in abundance at his feet. Birds sang in the trees, which grew straight and strong. At last Midreas's hopes soared – now his people would survive.

Many of his tribe wanted to settle immediately. Before making any decision Midreas climbed a small promontory to survey the area. Dorea accompanied him. "There are no rivers or lakes," he said. "While the land is rich compared to our lost continent, it is still not sufficient. We could survive here, but we would not thrive. Come, we shall continue east."

With the grumbling of the people loud in his ears, Midreas led them again towards the rising sun. "Take heart," he admonished them. "Not much further, and then we shall be able to make a new home."

As they travelled on, the land grew richer and more fertile.

Fir trees and birch grew in great forests and deer grazed in the clearings. The gatherers had no trouble in finding food.

Then, one day, one of the gatherers came running. "Midreas!" he said breathlessly. "I have seen a place and it might well be the new home for which we have been searching."

Midreas rose from the fire at which he had been warming himself. "Show me this place."

With Dorea, Midreas followed the excited gatherer over a small ridge. It was an easy climb over grass covered with animal droppings. The gatherers had no trouble hunting for food in this area, and Midreas was confident that the supply would remain good.

The gatherer stood at the top of the ridge, waiting for his leader to catch up. "There!" he said and pointed. Midreas looked. A broad river ran through a fertile valley. Gentle hills, covered with grass and woods, seemed to welcome him. In the still evening air, birds sang, and the wind blew softly through his hair and beard. He surveyed the area intently. It seemed good, but he was not yet certain. The land that would be a new home to his people must be all things to them. It would be their mother and father: their provider and protector. It must allow them to thrive.

Slowly, he turned westwards. The setting sun danced on the horizon. He stood motionless for a long time. There where the sun was setting rested the bones of his father, his family and friends. Atlantis was gone forever. Perhaps this new place would foster a new Atlantis.

The almost horizontal light struck his eyes, dazzling him. He turned again. The river, a flowing band of gold and red, reflected the setting sun, half blinding him. Eyes blurred, he thought that he could see a village of people. A group of houses erected at the river's edge, boats trolling the waters for fish and in a cleared grassy place, he thought he could see a great monument. A totem to the gods. Then, as his vision cleared, the earth, the water, the very air seemed to speak to him, and suddenly he found the decision easy.

"We shall settle here, in this gentle valley, beside the river. This will be the site of our new home. We shall build houses and farms, and we shall nurture our people. And one day, we shall build a monument in thanksgiving for our survival, and in testament to the knowledge of our people. From this time, we shall call this land The Place of the Sun and here with the gods' help we shall prosper."

Joyfully, the gatherer ran down the hill to tell the people of Midreas's decision.

3

It had not been a good day for Jonathan O'Neill, and it certainly didn't look like being a good night. Oh, the day had started out all right. He had managed to get to classes on time – a rather unusual feat for Jonathan. He was sitting in his desk when the bell rang, and Barnabus strode into the classroom, his long overcoat flapping in the breeze he had himself created, stopping only long enough to give his student a stare. "Well, Mr O'Neill. On time for a change, I see. And to what do we owe this rather unusual punctuality?"

His teacher touched his moustache briefly, the grey eyes glistening behind thick glasses. Suddenly, he put his hand to his head. "Ah! I think I have it! Could it have anything to do with the maths test today? And the rather unfortunate fact . . . " the man bent down slightly, staring squarely into Jonathan's eyes, " . . . that you, Mr O'Neill, are in danger of failing?" Jonathan turned red. A low rumble of stifled laughter came from his classmates. Barnabus straightened up suddenly. "I shouldn't think that there's any cause for laughter. Not in here! Might I remind you that almost half of this class is likely to face a similar fate!" The teacher muttered slightly, moving back up to the desk. "No matter. No matter. Let's see if we can do better this time. And Mr O'Neill? Might I remind you that a little concentration goes a long way?" As he uttered those words, Barnabus was gazing not unkindly at his pupil.

"Well, right you are," he continued. "Now, Miss Sullivan, if you'll hand out the test papers, we'll get on with it." The girl next to him, the one with the long brown hair, moved out of

16

her desk and up to the top of the classroom. Jonathan studied her as she moved. Cathy Sullivan lived on the same street. He did four of the same subjects as she did but as far as she was concerned, he might be living on Jupiter. Or one of its moons, anyway.

God, she's smart, he thought as she handed out the papers. He had tried to get her to help him. It wasn't that he wasn't smart enough or anything. But sometimes the equations just seemed so complicated. Cathy, on the other hand, was a whiz at maths. All she had to do was glance at an equation and the answer seemed to move from her brain to the point of her pencil with the speed of light. Jonathan needed help and Cathy was the one to give it. And he had to admit that the prospect of working alone with her a couple of hours a week was a fringe benefit that he wanted more than the actual lessons. Maybe he'd ask her again. Maybe today.

As he sat daydreaming he felt something burning into a point on his forehead. Barnabus was staring at him and it made him take his eyes off of Cathy and try to concentrate on the task ahead. That Barnabus! Jonathan thought. He is so damn demanding! He continued to consider his maths teacher. He was a fixture in the school and Jonathan remembered the first time that he had met him. It had been the first day at secondary school, and this bizarre character breezed into the classroom, a load of books and papers in his arms, stopping only long enough to drop the mess of papers and materials on to his desk.

Then he was up at the blackboard, scrawling his name, the chalk screeching along the surface. He turned back to the classroom. He still had his overcoat on and papers and pencils jutted from every pocket. For a full minute, he stared at his new charges, boring little holes into each forehead. Then he cleared his throat.

"Now!" He shouted it. One of the kids at the rear of the class actually jumped, startled, and the teacher glared at him with contempt. "As I was saying! My name is Barnabus. I repeat! Barnabus! Not Mr Barnabus or Dr Barnabus or

Professor Barnabus or any of that hogwash. Just *Barnabus*. I am your maths teacher and my objective is simple: I intend that you will understand everything that I teach you!"

That was Jonathan's introduction to the teacher. Since then, even though he never excelled in any of Barnabus's classes, he had tried to get along with him. If nothing else, the old guy tried to make maths interesting, and even Jonathan appreciated the effort. Most of the other teachers seemed to work on autopilot, apparently not caring about the subject or their pupils. But Barnabus was different.

A couple of times, when Jonathan had asked for the teacher's help, he had been invited out to his house. Barnabus lived a good few miles out of town, and Jonathan usually cycled there. Sometimes, he met Cathy at the house. She was there because she was the teacher's favourite. Jonathan was there as the teacher's pet albatross. But one thing that both students agreed about: Barnabus's house was fascinating.

The teacher was a bachelor and it showed. He never seemed to clean up. The sink was constantly choked with dirty dinner plates and cups; books and notes lay scattered on the floor. The windows needed washing. What fascinated them were the many shelves of books and the charts, maps, mobiles and pieces of experimental apparatus which lay about the place.

Barnabus was a man with many interests. Primarily a mathematician, he delved into many of the other sciences. His bookshelves held volumes on physics, engineering, archaeology, history and astronomy. From the ceiling of his living-room hung a complete model of the solar system, the nine scaled models circling a yellow globe that was the sun.

He was also interested in ancient megalithic engineering. Once, when both Cathy and Jonathan happened to be out at the house on the same day, they had helped Barnabus to complete a scale model of Stonehenge. When they had finished with the work, Barnabus showed them some of his other models: the pyramids, the Inca monuments, the great statues of Easter Island. As he showed them the models,

Barnabus taught them the many design and construction techniques which these ancient cultures had employed. "Look at the skills which these people used," he said to them. "To modern man, these techniques are simple. But thousands of years ago, these were major feats of engineering." He pointed to the model of Stonehenge. "See those plinths? The originals weigh many tonnes. Yet, megalithic man lifted them into position, carefully setting them on their uprights, without the aid of modern cranes. Indeed, they must have been a highly intelligent people."

He looked at each of them carefully. "The history of mankind is the foundation upon which we build today. By understanding the past we might live to understand tomorrow." Cathy and Jonathan could only look at each other. Barnabus had always seemed a little crazy. That said, he could glue them to the spot with a word or a phrase. He made Jonathan think a little, something that he didn't do enough of. And Jonathan quite liked thinking. He just wished that he could think as well as Cathy. But that was another matter.

He came out of the daydream again. Ah, yeah. The test. Cathy was there beside him, depositing a paper on his desk. She glanced at him. "Come on, O'Neill," she whispered at him. "Get it together. This is important!" He grinned at her foolishly. Yeah, he thought, well, maybe this isn't the best day to ask her for a grind. No. I just won't ask her. Then he looked at the paper and groaned. His classmates around him were uttering similar sounds. This was going to be horrible, he didn't know any of this. Then Barnabus spoke up, a devilish grin on his moustached face.

"As you know, now and again I like you to try to apply what you've learned to other areas of knowledge. Today, the topic is vector analysis. We've revised the formulae before and you have covered much of this stuff in physics anyway. You have an hour." He looked at them with some sympathy. "Take your time. It's not difficult. And try to do your best."

An hour later, Jonathan stood in the hall. So much for the test. He'd made a mess of it. He was sure of that. He stood against the wall, trying to recover. Then he saw Cathy. She walked over to him. "Hi," she said.

"Hi yourself."

"I take it you didn't do too well." She stood there, studying him.

"Nope. Can't say that I did." He stood awkwardly, trying to muster up some courage. Go on, ask her! She can only say no. "I was wondering. You know this stuff pretty well, don't you?"

Now it was her turn to stand awkwardly. "I guess so. Maths has always come easily to me."

He laughed a little. "Sure. And so have physics and chemistry and biology. You're good at the stuff, Cathy."

She smiled, embarrassed. "Yeah, I guess so."

He looked at her, not sure what to say next. "Look," he said finally, "I need some help. Otherwise I'm sure to fail and I can forget passing the Leaving. I know I've asked before but I was wondering if you'd mind going through some of his stuff with me?"

"I don't know, Jonathan." She stood looking at him. God, she's really pretty, he thought. "Look. I'm not too good at teaching people. Why don't you ask Barnabus to give you some tutoring?"

"Oh, I've done some extra classes with him. You know that. It just doesn't seem to help."

"What makes you think I can help?"

He shook his head. "I don't know. Barnabus just seems to make things so . . . strange sometimes. I mean, what he says is simple enough. But then he starts talking about Egyptian mummies or Inca sacrifices or something, and I lose my train of thought."

She stared down the hall, considering. "Well, maybe. Look, let me think about it. Why don't you come over to my house tonight? Just for a while. We can talk about it."

Jonathan felt electricity pour through him. "Hey, great! What time?"

"Say about eight."

"Sure. Fine. Hey, I'll see you! Yeah! Eight o'clock. See you then, Cath!" He walked away, still watching her and bumped into Sean Harris, a mate of his, sending his books flying everywhere, and not apologising or stopping to help because he never felt the impact.

Hey! he thought. This is great! Maybe some things are going to change!

Jonathan arrived outside her house at exactly eight o'clock. He stood nervously, looking at the stars in the clear April sky. For a change, it wasn't raining, and in the fresh evening air he thought about the girl he was going to see.

She was quite something – the ultimate mathematics wizard at school. She also admitted to an aptitude in physics and biology and wanted to study astrophysics and space technology at university. She had long recognised that she'd probably not be able to study these subjects in Ireland and was starting to consider her options. Barnabus was aware of her plans, however, and had already been in touch with two universities in the United States. Both CalTech and MIT had good courses in her chosen fields, and said that they would consider taking her on a full scholarship.

She never said very much in class. Jonathan thought that she was something of a snob but he was wrong. She was just shy and covered it up by staying quiet. And she could seem to be really cold when it suited her. It was a cover. She didn't want anyone to know how much she really wanted to go into space. She thought that her friends, her classmates, her parents, even, wouldn't take her seriously. And she was right.

Now, Jonathan stood at the door. He swallowed hard and pressed the doorbell. It took ages but the wooden door finally swung open. "Hey, how'r'ya doin'?" he asked roughly.

She studied him for a moment. "Do you always talk like that?"

"Like what?" he asked defensively.

"Like a moron." He stood looking at her with a hurt expression. She sighed and held the door open. "All right. Come on in."

"Yeah. Right." He walked into the hallway, looking around. He'd never been in the house before, even though they lived in the same street. "Where to?"

She pointed up the stairs. "Upstairs?" he asked.

"Yes. My parents are in the living-room. We'll go up to my bedroom."

He smiled broadly. "Your bedroom?"

"Yes. And don't get any funny ideas."

"No! No, honest. We're just going to study."

She walked up the stairs, Jonathan following. She opened the door to her room and Jonathan stood staring in amazement. Covering every wall were reminders of Cathy's vocation. In one corner, a poster of the Orion nebula hung, the dust clouds lit brilliantly from behind. In another, was a full colour blow-up of Saturn. On the far wall, a huge poster of Albert Einstein stared out at them, the face of the great mathematician seeming to pose infinite questions and to know infinite solutions.

"Hey, this is great!" He walked in, moving over to the telescope that stood in a corner. He touched it lightly.

"Be careful with that, Jonathan. That's an eight-inch Newtonian telescope. It's not cheap."

"Oh yeah. Right." He walked around it. "You really use this thing?"

"Sure I do. On clear nights I can see the rings of Saturn, the moons of Jupiter, the mountain peaks surrounding the Moon's seas."

"You really like this stuff, don't you, Cathy?"

She nodded a little. "Yes. It's what I want to do."

He laughed. "What? You want to go into space or something? Be an astronaut? Hey, that's really funny."

"It's not funny." She was suddenly angry, her blue eyes turning to ice. "It's what I want to do. And you don't have to laugh about it."

"Hey, I'm sorry. I didn't mean anything. You know, though, you've got one problem. Ireland doesn't have a space programme."

"I know that," she said scornfully, then wistfully she continued. "Sometimes, Jonathan, I wish that I didn't live in Ireland. I wish I lived in Russia or America. Even France. Somewhere that had an active space exploration programme." She sat down on the bed and looked across the room at one of the posters. It was the great galaxy of Andromeda. Its swirl of stars looking like the vortex of a whirlpool. "That's my only dream. To go out there. It's so beautiful. It's all I really want."

He came across and sat by her. God, she's beautiful, he thought. She was dressed simply. No make-up or anything. With eyes like those, who needed make-up?

"Well, if that's what you want to do, Cathy, you should just go on out there and do it."

She looked at him hopefully. "Do you really think so?"

"Sure. Why not. Who's going to stop you? I think it's great that you're so ambitious."

Cathy moved closer to him, her eyes bright with excitement. God, he thought, if she gets any closer I'm going to – to what? He looked at her, her lips moving, but he couldn't hear a thing. He only watched.

" . . . so you see, it should be pretty straightforward. I'll get my degree in astrophysics at CalTech or MIT, then apply to NASA. Barnabus thinks I should have a good chance."

"What?" Jonathan looked at her, a little dazed. "What did you say?"

She smiled. "I said I should have a good chance." She moved even closer to him. He swallowed hard. Come on stupid, he said to himself. Say something.

"Well, you know. It's like I said. I think that's great. Ah . . . " He swallowed. "You know, I hate to say it. But it is a long shot, don't you think?"

Cathy stared at him.

Oh no, I've said the wrong thing. Come on, talk! "Not that you wouldn't be successful or anything," he blustered. "But I hear it's incredibly competitive. And even if you start now, I mean most of the astronauts are pilots, aren't they? I mean, I'm sure there are some pure scientists but most of them have learned how to fly. And you don't have any flying experience, do you?"

That's not the thing to say either, he thought, mentally kicking himself.

"No, I don't," she said coldly.

"Not that it's absolutely necessary to be a pilot, you know. I'm sure it will all work out for you. Sure! MIT, CalTech, NASA, then, someday, who knows? You'll be blasting off into the great unknown. The first Irishwoman in outer space. I think that's great."

She sat on the bed, saying nothing. "I think you'd better leave, Jonathan."

He looked at her. She stared back, unmoving. "Right. Uh, I think maybe it's time to go." He got up from the bed and crossed the room. He turned to her. "I guess that the grind is out of the question."

She glared back at him. "You guessed right. Get Barnabus to help you out."

"Well, I'll see you tomorrow."

"Yes. Close the door on your way out."

"No problem." He went down the stairs, back out into the April evening, and closed the front door behind him. The stars were twinkling, and he could see the vast river of light that was the Milky Way. It reminded him of Cathy. So bright, so far away. Jonathan sighed and walked home.

Nope. All in all it had been a pretty horrible day. He'd messed up a maths test, pissed Cathy off but otherwise was doing . . . just lousy. Now, he sat in the living-room in his father's easy-chair. The maths book was propped up on his knees, and he tried to study it while gnawing at an apple.

"Jonathan." His father's voice came in through the open kitchen door.

"Yeah?" He looked up, half expecting his dad to come roaring through the door but nothing happened.

"You know what time it is?"

"Let me guess. Nine o'clock?"

"How about eleven? Come on, time to go to bed."

Jonathan thought, I'm seventeen. I'm old enough to decide for myself when to go to bed. "Come on. I gotta study this stuff."

"If you want to study, you should do it when you come in from school. Now, bed!"

He shook his head. Some things never change. He made his way up the stairs. At the top he took hold of the banister knob. It came off in his hand. He yelled down the stairs. "Hey, Dad! This banister is still broken."

"I'll fix it tomorrow."

"Yeah, sure." It had been broken for over a month. He put the knob back and went into the bathroom. Then he went into his bedroom, undressed, and got into bed. God, he thought, I have to get out of here. Nothing's ever going to change. Not the banister knob. Or maths. Or Cathy. Nothing. He reached over, turned out the light on the bedside table and fell asleep.

The sound of thunder woke him up. He sat up in bed thinking that he had been dreaming. Then it happened again. The room filled for a moment with the flash of light, throwing his furniture into stark relief. Then, seconds later, the thunder rolled in through the open window. He pushed back the covers and crawled out of bed. Jonathan looked groggily at the clock. Half past three. Slowly, he made his way over to the window. This is strange, he thought. The atmosphere didn't seem heavy enough for thunder.

He stood looking out the open window, shivering a little in the cool April breeze. His house was situated on a small hill. From the window he could see far out to the east.

Out on the horizon, lit up by great flashes of lightning, he could see huge storm clouds. As he watched, a long sliver of light shot from cloud to cloud. He started to count. One second for each mile from the storm. His crazy father had taught him that. He counted sixteen and the sound of thunder rolled in through the open window. As he stood, the storm intensified, with great arcs of lightning filling the sky, lighting up his room. Yet the storm seemed to be standing still, and he wondered what it was like right underneath it. I'll bet those people over there are petrified, he thought.

Then, something else happened. At first, he thought he was dreaming, it was so weird. He leaned out the window, trying to be certain. "Wow! It has to be real."

A beam of light, almost like a searchlight but far more intense, arced suddenly through the sky. He shook his head. "That's no lightning," he thought. He'd never seen anything like it. He was sure that its origin was on the ground. Way over there, maybe fifteen miles away. It flashed up from beyond the hills, illuminating the storm clouds, cutting through them like some sort of huge search light.

He watched it for almost a full minute. As he watched, it moved, swinging around the points of the compass, as if searching for something. Then as suddenly as it started, it stopped.

And that was it. He watched for ten more minutes. The storm seemed to have stopped when the great beam vanished. As he watched, the clouds parted, and behind them the stars floated in the mist of pre-dawn. Jonathan shivered slightly and went back to bed. "Heck!" he whispered, thinking about what he had seen. "What the hell was that?"

4

"Y ou mean you saw it, too?"

Jonathan was in the maths class, Cathy sitting beside him, waiting for Barnabus to appear. He'd have the results of the maths test with him and Jonathan could already visualise the series of little red marks covering the pages.

"Yes. I saw it. It was the strangest thing I've ever seen."

Jonathan nodded. "You don't think it was a searchlight or anything like that, do you?"

Cathy gazed at him. "Come on, Jonathan. Do you think it looked like a searchlight?"

"I guess you're right. It was too bright, wasn't it?"

"Definitely. And that thunderstorm. It was huge."

They both sat thinking about it. He turned to her. "Cathy . . . "
"Yes?"

"Look. I hope I didn't say anything to make you mad last night."

"Oh, no. Of course you didn't, Jonathan. You just wrecked my dream. That's all."

"Oh." He squirmed in his chair. "Would it help if I apologised?"

She considered for a moment. "Maybe."

"Well, then, I apologise."

She stared at him. "And that makes it all right?"

He looked back at her. "Did you know that when you get mad, your eyes glitter?"

She sat for a moment, not knowing what to say. "You know, Jonathan, you can be a real ass at times."

He smiled. "Friends?" he asked.

"If you like."

"Good. Now, where were we? Yeah, that storm." He looked at her sheepishly. "Hey, I hope I don't sound dumb, or anything. But that storm was a real freak, don't you think so? I mean, it didn't move or anything. It just sat there. And then that light . . . "

Cathy nodded in agreement. "I noticed that, too. I didn't know what to think."

"The weirdest thing, though, was the way the storm just stopped."

"It stopped when the light went out, didn't it?" Cathy sat thinking. "As if the light somehow controlled the storm."

"Yeah. That's what I thought. It was weird."

They both sat then, thinking about it. The more Jonathan thought, the more it didn't make sense. A beam of light just couldn't control a storm. Could it?

The commotion in the hall outside the classroom shook Jonathan back into reality. The principal, Mr McManus, walked suddenly into the classroom and stood behind Barnabus's desk. The little man waited for the class to be quiet.

"I'm sorry to tell you that Barnabus won't be in today." His voice seemed somehow strained. "You can take the rest of the period as study time. If Barnabus can't join us tomorrow for any reason, Mrs Andrews will take over his classes."

Jonathan stared at the principal for a moment. "You mean Barnabus won't be in tomorrow? Where is he?"

The principal squirmed a little. He coughed slightly, covering his mouth. "Well, to be honest, we're not certain. He left no message." He cleared his throat again. "It seems that Barnabus is missing. The gardaí may have to be called. We don't know when Barnabus left, or where he has gone. We can only assume that he's been delayed somewhere. That's all the information I have." He turned to the rest of the class. "Now, given the circumstances, I would appreciate it if you would all get down to work."

The class broke out in a muffled explosion of questions;

then quietened under the glare of the principal. Then, as the pupils opened their books, the principal left the room. Cathy and Jonathan looked meaningfully at each other, gathered their books and slipped out, leaving the school by the back entrance.

They pedalled their bicycles fast along the river road, past the old cemetery. Then they turned right, up the hill, and after some hard pedalling made the summit. The teacher's farmhouse was at the top of the hill. The drive was empty, the ancient Morris Minor gone. The house seemed deserted.

They stood for a minute, looking. "He's not here!"

"Hey, great! What a deduction." Cathy dismounted, laying her bike down on the drive. "Come on, let's try the door."

Jonathan walked up to the front entrance. "Locked," he said. He stood, uncertain what to do. "Maybe one of the windows is open."

"We can't just break in."

Jonathan looked at her. "Come on. Take some risks, Cathy. Our teacher is missing, for heaven's sake. Anyway, we won't be breaking in. We'll be investigating. There's a difference."

"Some difference," she replied crossly. "All right. You go that way." She pointed toward the side of the house. "I'll try the other side. If you find something, yell."

They went off in different directions, searching for an opening into the house. Jonathan tried the back door. It was locked, as was the back window. He tried the kitchen window but that was locked, too. Looking through it, he could see unwashed cups and breakfast plates on the table. They looked as if they had been there for a while. An open carton of milk stood on the draining-board. He knew that his teacher was untidy, but it seemed odd that Barnabus hadn't put the milk back in the refrigerator.

"Must have been in a hurry," said Jonathan to himself. He made his way across the small yard to the old barn. It needed paint badly. Weeds grew against the walls, and Jonathan walked through them, pushing his way towards the door. It was open, and he stepped into darkness. It took a second for his eyes to adjust. He had never been in here before. The place was a mess, just like the house. An old bicycle stood against the wall. Tins of paint, covered in dust, cluttered a set of shelves. He looked slowly around the barn, trying to get his bearings. One corner of the room appeared more organised than the rest. Jonathan picked his way carefully past old furniture and an ancient washing machine. Finally, he stood in front of a workbench. He recognised a laptop computer and some pieces of electronic testing equipment. The rest of the stuff puzzled him. Banks of electronics gear were organised carefully on a series of shelves. A variety of tools – electrical pliers, soldering irons and screwdrivers – lay on the workbench. Some spare transistors and diodes lay in small boxes, and a range of microprocessors were still in their plastic factory packaging. It looked as if his teacher had been working on something.

The door opened behind him, the room filling with sunlight. "What's in here?"

He turned to Cathy. "Look at this stuff." She walked over to him, through the maze of junk. "He was working on something. I didn't know that he was into electronics, too."

Cathy took in the workbench and its contents. "Well, whatever he was working on, it's not here. Come on. I think I found a way in." Jonathan glanced back at the workbench, puzzled, and followed her out of the barn.

The bedroom window was unlocked, but it was sealed shut with numerous coats of paint. Jonathan tried to open it but it wouldn't budge. He turned to Cathy, breathing hard from the effort. "I thought I saw a crowbar back in the barn."

"Jonathan! We can't just lever open the window with a crowbar. We could break something." He just stared at her. "OK, OK. Get the crowbar." She stood with her arms crossed. He fetched the steel bar and lodged it between the window and the frame. Then he pushed. The wooden ledge of the window broke, and a pane of glass shattered. He moved the bar a little. Finally, he had it open.

"Barnabus is going to kill us for breaking that window."

He motioned to her. "He won't say a thing. Now let's go in." Jonathan climbed in first, then helped Cathy.

Though it was late morning, the house was dark. They knew that Barnabus preferred it that way. "Turn on some lights. Let's see what we can find."

They started with the bedrooms. They had entered the house through the guestroom. Here the bed was made. Nothing seemed to have been disturbed. "Come on. Let's try Barnabus's bedroom."

"You shouldn't go in there."

"Cathy, I'm only going to look around." He opened the door. Here, it looked as if someone had been in a hurry. The wardrobe door was open and hangers littered the floor. All the drawers of the chest were pulled open. Socks and shirts lay in a tangle, some on the floor, others flung on the bed.

"Looks like he was packing," Cathy said.

Jonathan looked around the room again. "Come on. Let's try the rest of the house."

They walked into the kitchen. Jonathan retrieved the milk carton from the clutter on the table. "The milk's warm," he stated.

"So?"

He stared at her. "Hey, who's the one with the mighty intellect here? It's morning, right? If he had been in the house this morning the milk should be cold. Or cool, anyway. My guess is that he hasn't been here since we saw him yesterday in class."

"So what? So he chose to spend a night away?"

"Get with it, Cathy. You know Barnabus as well as I do. He never goes away. He's always locked up in his study." He thought for a second. "Come on. We'll try there next."

They went down the hall. The familiar oak door was closed. Jonathan put his hand on the doorknob and turned it. Slowly, he opened the door. They stood at the doorway, looking in at the mess in front of them.

Their teacher was untidy but they'd never known him to be like this. It looked as if a bomb had exploded in the room. All the furniture was pushed back against the walls. Books and notes, the models of Stonehenge and the pyramids, his typewriter and school texts, lay in a heap in one corner. That was nothing compared to what was in the middle of the room, however.

"Look at that," Cathy whispered. In the centre of the room, in the exact centre, was a scaled model of the megalithic burial mound at Newgrange. It was big. Huge. Filling the room. Around it, dried mud flecked the floor. And next to the giant model papers lay scattered, as if abandoned there by someone in a hurry.

The two looked at each other. "Holy Mary," Cathy said. "What's he up to now?"

5

Midreas made every effort to ensure the survival of his people. The Atlanteans had arrived at the Place of the Sun in the early spring. Midreas immediately began to do what was necessary so that they would live through the next year.

With Dorea, he surveyed the new lands. Leaving his tribe to gather what food they could, he travelled over the ridge of gentle hills, descending into a small valley. The land was rich and fertile and he knew that life-sustaining crops could be grown here. He walked on through a copse of trees and down a bank of rough heather, until he came at last to a gently flowing river. He stood for a while in thought. The sun warmed his shoulders, and he tasted the clean smell of the river and heard birds singing as they searched for food. Midreas turned slowly, looking back up the hill, and what he saw pleased him greatly. His people would survive and prosper here, and in their prosperity, they would have time to study the scrolls which his father Psorsis had given to them. It was Midreas's task now to make certain that they lived to carry on the work of his father and to rebuild their culture.

Turning to Dorea, he said, "We shall build our homes here." That night, as they huddled by a makeshift fire eating last year's fruits and rabbit which the gatherers had trapped, he outlined his plans to his architects and engineers. The next morning they started.

The arduous journey from their destroyed continent had taken the lives of almost half his tribe. To ensure the survival of those remaining, builders were instructed to raise family houses and storage barns. About one hundred men and women toiled in the woods, the sounds of their flint axes echoing across the valley as they cut timber. Others stripped the branches of their leaves and cut them into working lengths. Others again dug the post holes which would hold the uprights for the wooden buildings.

Midreas stayed with his workers, ensuring that they understood what must be done. More than once, stripped to the waist, he helped his men to drag the heavy timbers across the fields, and he raised his own axe to cut the wood into lengths. His people saw the sweat on his brow, and they knew that Psorsis, his father, had sired a leader of men.

When the building programme was well under way, Midreas turned his attention to the food supply. For an entire night, he worked with Dorea, determining how much food his people would require to live.

"We know nothing of this land or its climate," Dorea said to him. "We do not know what the land will yield or what crops it will grow. And we have eaten the seed which we had brought with us. We have none left to plant new crops."

Midreas considered carefully what she said to him. Then he replied, "We don't know what the land will yield, therefore we shall have to guess. I have seen wild oats and barley as I walked through the valley, and I know that these will grow. We have no seed left but our gatherers will harvest the wild grain and from this we will grow a new crop. In the meantime, we shall live off the land. We know that rabbits abound in these woods, and I have seen the droppings of deer, fox and mice. We shall hunt these. The fields are filled with the calls of many birds. These too we shall hunt. Our fishermen shall fish in the river, and our gatherers will go through the lands in search of edible plants and fruits. We shall survive until the new crop can be harvested."

The very next day, he sent his gatherers to harvest the wild grain; his hunters began their search for game; his fishermen took nets to the river. He called his cultivators to sit with him, and together they devised a plan to plough certain tracts of land to make them ready for planting.

By the end of the third month, Midreas's people were housed in rough huts covered in the grass of the fields. The hunters and gatherers were providing food for them. The farmers were awaiting the new harvest of wild grain. In this month, too, one of the women gave birth to a baby, and in honour of her leader, she named the boy Midreas. On that day, the leader knew that his people would flourish.

Now the longest days of the year were upon them. Midreas gave his people leave to lay down their work, and for two days they celebrated their survival. The people rested, basking in the summer sun and bathing naked in the river. He looked at all that they had accomplished, and he was proud of them.

One night, Midreas chose to sleep in the open. He had done so as a boy, and he remembered the peace which he had felt, lying in a field not far from the great capital of their people. Now the city was gone, but the night sky remained. Midreas lay facing the stars, and, as he watched, he saw a meteor fall through the sky. He watched it burn to nothingness, and he thought again about the comet which had come through the heavens to destroy his people. One day, he believed, such another might come again. And on that day, his people must be prepared.

The dawn came early, and Midreas raised himself, stiff from sleeping in the grass, and wiped the morning dew from his face. Refreshed, he climbed on to the ridge of hills that surrounded the valley. He made his way carefully along a narrow deer trail, until at last he came to a pile of stones. Weeks before, he had instructed some of his men to gather rocks from the river bed. These rocks had been rounded and smoothed by the action of the waters. With difficulty, they had carried them up the valley slopes to this level place.

With help from others, he brought up the vessel which carried the scrolls of Psorsis. It had rested in his hut but now he meant to protect it further. The vessel remained unopened. The time for study would come, but not in his lifetime. He placed the casket in the centre of the field, and aided by his men, covered the vessel carefully with rocks until a small cairn rose above it.

Now he stood at the base of that cairn, and looked out at the small village newly built on the valley floor. He rested awhile, his hands upon the rock, feeling near to his father. He sat for a long time, thinking. It was true that his people were safe but he had to admit that much had been lost. From great cities, they were reduced to living in wooden huts. They no longer had schools of learning, or huge factories, or the shared wisdom of a great people. Nor did they have the time or tools to rebuild these things. Their time was consumed by the rudiments of survival. Their schools of learning were reduced to teaching the basic skills of how to live in a new land. Any factories they built would be for the production of simple implements and tools. This was the fate of the Atlanteans, at least for the present.

His hands touched the rock, warmed by the sun. Beneath, the knowledge of his father rested, and Midreas knew that some day this same knowledge would restore the people to their former greatness – and beyond. At all costs, the scrolls must be protected.

He sat for the entire day until the sun set beyond the valley wall. Squinting in the glare of the sun, Midreas came to a decision. On this site would rise a great monument. It would be a monument to his father. To his people. A monument of what they had been, and what they would become again. And it would also be something else . . .

In the heart of the monument would rest the scrolls of Psorsis, protected for the moment, awaiting that time when the people would once again be ready to learn. Midreas might never live to see the completion of this monument, so great would its structure be. But his decision to build it would give him comfort for the rest of his life.

At peace, Midreas descended into the valley again, back to the poor wooden huts of his people.

6

The model of Newgrange was big. Huge. It filled the room. It was at least fifteen feet across, maybe three feet high. Jonathan and Cathy were stunned by it. "Look at the detail!" Cathy said. "I've never seen anything like it." The model was an exact replica of the famous megalithic burial mound located outside Slane, some thirty-five miles north of Dublin. Barnabus had been exact in his model-making, as usual. Grass grew on top of the mound, green turf cropped close to its surface. One side of the mound was covered with fine quartz chippings which sparkled in the morning light that now streamed through the study window.

On that side was the entrance – a small opening propped up with lintels and stone risers. Above that was a small box aperture. Jonathan knew the purpose of that. In the real Newgrange, at winter solstice – the shortest day of the year – the sun rises over the horizon and shines through the exact centre of this aperture. Barnabus had explained that this was how the people of ancient Ireland honoured their dead. The opening faced the window of the study. The sunlight struck it, bouncing and shimmering across the quartz which surrounded it.

In front of the door was a large slab of rock, resting on its side. On its surface, Barnabus had carved the fine whorls and curves – the ancient megalithic art – for which Newgrange was famous. Carefully, Jonathan knelt and touched the carvings. He felt a sense of power, as if the stone slab and the mound itself were transmitting a force into his hand and up his arm – into his entire body.

"Jonathan, come here and look at this." Cathy had walked behind the mound. "You've been to Newgrange, haven't you?"

"Sure," he said. "Any time we have visitors, we take them over. I've been there, I don't know, maybe a dozen times. Why? Haven't you?"

"Yes, of course. But it's years since I've been there." She stood, not quite understanding what she looked at. Finally, she motioned to him to join her.

"You ever notice this before?" Cathy pointed. Another entrance was cut into the mound, directly opposite the front opening. This one was larger than the front entrance, a square portal over a foot high. It was framed in risers and a lintel, and each part of the stone frame was decorated in the same carved swirls found at the front entrance.

Jonathan looked at Cathy. "I've never seen this." He hesitated slightly. "I mean, I know what is there, of course. It's a huge carved kerbstone. Not as big as the one in the front, but pretty amazing all the same. It has a weird combination of carvings on it. Whorls and diamonds and holes, all carved in this pattern. But one thing I'm really certain of – the monument doesn't have a rear door."

"Then why did Barnabus put it in?" They stood staring at it.

"I don't know. He does everything to scale. He is a perfectionist when it comes to details. "

Cathy looked slowly up at Jonathan. "Which means, of course, that it must be there."

"I told you, Cathy. All that's there is this stone carving."

"Don't you see? Barnabus found something important, something which no one else has seen before. That entrance *must* be there."

She walked over to the side of the model and picked up and tidied a drift of papers which littered the floor. She then cleared a table. Carefully, she laid out the papers. Jonathan came over to stand by her. "What are those?"

"I'm not sure. See?" She pointed to a series of drawings.

"Sketches of the mound. Almost a diagram. Those are compass headings. West. North. East. South. The front entrance to Newgrange faces almost directly due east. And look at these lines." With her finger, she traced a series of circles. Each circle began and ended in the exact centre of the mound. "Two series of non-concentric circles, all having a single junction point. One set of circles to the north, the other to the south." She looked at Jonathan. "Like a magnetic field, Jonathan."

"That's right. As if the Newgrange monument were a giant electro-magnet."

She turned a page. The next page showed a side view of the mound. In the drawing, the sun rose to the east and its rays were drawn as a series of lines entering the front aperture. A series of waves projected from the rear entrance, out and up, and over the horizon to the west. In the margins were a series of mathematical calculations.

"Any ideas?"

Cathy shook her head. "I'm lost. That's differential calculus. And see that? It's a formula for kinetic energy." She stared down at the page. "I'd say Barnabus is calculating power outputs of some kind. That's all that I can figure."

Jonathan's mouth was open. "Power outputs? From Newgrange?"

"That's what it looks like."

"Ah, come on. That's crazy. You mean that Barnabus thinks that Newgrange is emitting power of some kind?" He shook his head and his voice rose. "Even Barnabus isn't *that* much off the wall. That place is over five thousand years old, for Pete's sake. It's dead! It can't generate power. Look at it!" He turned, facing the model. "It's just stone and clay and grass. It's impossible. Barnabus must be crazy. The guy's gone absolutely crackers. If he thinks that this big dead hill can generate a force of some kind, he's nuts!"

The door opened. Barnabus strode into the room, his overcoat covered with dirt. A peculiar smile was set on his face. He looked at his model briefly, then at Jonathan.

"Well, Jonathan," he said, hands thrust deeply into his overcoat. "I simply must be nuts, then!"

"Barnabus. Barnabus! Come on, slow down!" Jonathan cried as the teacher ran madly around the room, his overcoat flapping against his knees. From the table, he gathered his papers.

"Get my briefcase, Jonathan, if you don't mind."

"But Barnabus . . . "

"Ah!" The scholar put a single finger in the air. "No time for talk. No questions, all right?" He smiled at the puzzled look on the student's face. "Just the briefcase. Go and get it."

"Where is it?"

"In the kitchen." He turned to Cathy. "Grab the star charts. They're in the bookcase. And get my reference notes marked 'Physical Aberrations.' Oh, hold on. I might have them." He felt in his pockets, which were bulging with notes. "Never mind, I have them here." He ran out the door.

Cathy stood looking at Jonathan. "What are we going to do?"

He shrugged. "I don't know. Let's humour him. I'll get the briefcase. You find those star charts. I just hope that Barnabus won't have to be put away."

Cathy nodded. "Agreed." Jonathan turned and went out to the kitchen door. Cathy went over to the bookcase and found the astronomy section. She removed a folder marked "Star charts." Then she went to find her teacher.

Barnabus was in the bedroom. A small suitcase lay on the bed. Barnabus was throwing clothes into it.

"Where are you going?"

He looked at her, opening his mouth then closing it again, not knowing what to say. Then he started to laugh. "I . . . I don't know, to be honest with you," he said, "I'm not certain. Wherever the stars take me, I imagine." He threw an old coat on top of the pile of clothing and struggled to close the case. "Give me a hand with this." Cathy tried to help him close it as Jonathan came into the room, holding the briefcase. He stood watching the two struggle with the suitcase. His teacher looked up, spotting him.

"Well, don't just stand there, lad. Give us a hand here." Jonathan sat on top of the case. Barnabus latched it. He stood suddenly. "Right! Now, to food! Back to the kitchen!"

"Look, Barnabus." Cathy and Jonathan followed their teacher down the hall and into the kitchen. "Won't you tell us what's going on? You know, you should at least ring the school – tell them you're here. They'll have the guards out looking for you."

The teacher merely waved a hand at them. "No time. No time! And if I told them, they wouldn't believe me, anyway. Come on, give us a hand." Barnabus started throwing things into the open briefcase. Tins of beans, biscuits, anything that came to hand. He tried to close the case. It wouldn't catch either. "Too much!" he said, and dumped half of the contents on the floor. The briefcase closed. "Perfect!" He paused, trying to get his bearings.

Cathy stared at her teacher. "Barnabus, don't you think that you could just tell us . . . "

Both hands went up in the air. "Great God! I almost forgot!" He turned to them. "Come on you two, if you want to help – this way." He marched back out the door.

"What'll we do?"

"I don't know. Follow him, I suppose." Jonathan picked up the suitcase. "Grab his briefcase."

"I'm phoning the guards."

"Hang on a minute. Let's see what this is all about first." He motioned to her. "Come on. Let's find him."

They found him out in the barn. Barnabus was standing at the workbench, looking at the materials scattered around him. He turned and saw them standing at the door, not certain what to do or say. "Come on, come on." He waved at them. "If you're going to help, get over here." They retraced the path to the workbench. He stood thinking for a moment. "To forget the most important elements! Jonathan, maybe you're right. Maybe I am out of my mind." He stood muttering to himself, picking up one tool, then another. "What to take. What to take!" He glanced at Cathy. "Here, give me that briefcase." She handed it to him. She watched as he reopened it, and dumped the food out into a pile on the workbench. "I'll just have to worry about food when I get there. Now, let's see. Tools." He began hurling things into the case. "Portable soldering iron. Screwdriver set. Diodes. Resistors. Five, no, six spare microprocessors. Just in case." He looked up, smiling. "Just to be on the safe side, you know. Now what else?" He studied the bench. "Pliers. Some wire. That should do it." He slammed the briefcase shut, securing the lock.

Finally, he turned to the laptop computer. He switched it on for a moment, looking intently at the flickering screen. "Good. Batteries are fully charged!" Then, he switched it off, disconnecting it, closing and locking the cover. "That's everything then." He turned quickly, dust flying around him. "All right! That's it. Out to the car!"

"Barnabus! Hey, Barnabus!" called Jonathan. But he was gone again, threading his way out of the barn, Jonathan and Cathy in his wake. He walked quickly through the yard and out to the Morris Minor. Opening the door, he shoved the laptop computer and the briefcase into the back seat. He turned, grabbing the suitcase from Jonathan. He threw that into the passenger seat.

Then he made his way around to the driver's door. He got into the car, and opened the window. Inserting the key, he turned it, and the ancient motor caught. "Fine. All ready now, I think!" He looked out the window at the students who were standing by the side of the car, Cathy hanging on to the door handle. "Well, no time for formal goodbyes. I'll see you when I return."

"But Barnabus!" Cathy was close to tears. She stood, hand clutching the door tightly .

"Sorry, my little mathematician. No time for speeches or even for a parting handshake! Give my regards to the students at school. Cheerio, now! Cheerio!"

He ground the old car into reverse, and put the accelerator to the floor. Cathy had to let go of the handle. The Morris shot out of the drive, coming to rest on the embankment on the far side of the road. Cathy and Jonathan ran out the drive after the car.

"Hey! Come on! Can't you at least tell us where you're going?"

He looked at them, smiling. "Into the distant unknown. That's all I'll say. Goodbye now!" Barnabus put the car into gear, and accelerated off down the road, disappearing over the hill.

Jonathan and Cathy stood in the middle of the road, staring after him. Cathy turned to Jonathan. "Any idea where he's gone?"

"Only one place I can think of." Jonathan glanced at her. "Newgrange. Come on. Grab your bike."

7

Now that the refugees from Atlantis had at last found a suitable place to settle and rebuild their civilisation, their first task was to devise a structure which would not only protect the treasured scrolls of Psorsis but which would also be a testament to their survival.

Engineers, architects and archaeologists of the twentieth century marvel at the sheer size, bulk and accuracy with which the megalithic mound at Newgrange was built. Thousands of tonnes of rock were laid in precise locations, set exactly in a prescribed geometric design. Without the aid of modern tools, the builders accomplished a tremendous feat of engineering, using knowledge passed down from their forefathers. Today, some pseudo-scientists argue that Newgrange was the work of Stone Age gods, the result of magical powers which today's humankind has lost. To some extent, they may be right. But what many have not considered is the sheer intellectual brilliance of the Atlanteans, their determination and patience.

When Midreas sat down with his architects, huddled around a fire on a cool autumn evening, he explained to them what he wanted. He envisaged a place of fantastic proportions, a design which echoed the greatness of their lost cities, so tragically destroyed. He required a central area which would protect the scrolls, keep them safe until such time as his people would be able to unlock the secrets of his father. But he wanted something else, too. He wanted the structure to be able to tap into whatever power sources the earth and sun offered. He could only guess at what the scrolls of his father held, but he sensed that implementing his father's work would require power. And that power must be adequate for any need which his children might have. He determined that he would give the future this resource.

To do this, he drew upon the knowledge of the earth and nature which his people had long held. The Atlanteans had developed a culture which was in harmony with the world around them. Unlike modern men, they could sense forces of nature which today can be detected only with sophisticated equipment. They harnessed sunlight, and were able to detect and control the forces of magnetism. They also understood the physical properties of certain rock formations, and knew of the great potential and kinetic energy held in water and in the heart of the earth itself.

In picking his site for the monument, Midreas let his mind search for a point where these natural forces coalesced, where the potential energy would be greatest. The site which he chose was high up the valley wall, in full view of the rising sun. This as yet untapped solar power would, he knew, be a great source of energy to future generations. Also, he sensed the positive magnetic forces which surrounded the site, which generations to come could utilise for as yet unknown purposes. Putting out his hands, he divined the great sources of water energy buried far below the surface. He knew that spiralling waters poured relentlessly through blind and underground rivers far beneath his feet. And even further below, the great core of the earth churned, spending itself in changing the face of the world through great shifts in its power. Here, Midreas would build his monument. He would build it within the confines of this energy supply, on a site with strong magnetic fields and in the direct line of the sun.

For building materials, he sent his gatherers and engineers far afield. The great river which had carved their valley carried boulders and other materials which would be used for decorative work. The surrounding countryside would provide the clays to fill crevices. But for the supporting structure, he had to find certain materials which were unavailable in the immediate area.

For months they searched. After five months, an engineer returned to report finding a valley of lakes and streams far to the south. The walls of this valley held a treasure trove of huge silica deposits. These, the engineer knew, could be easily split into great shale slabs suitable for the basic structure.

One early morning soon afterwards, with the rain falling, Midreas set out with a band of ten men to view the deposits for himself. The engineer, Torcas, led them south over plains and gently rolling hills. After four days' journey they came to a series of higher hills, almost mountains. A sea lapped gently against a sandy beach to the east, and a few miles inland a great conical mountain filled the horizon.

From here, the going was heavier. Torcas led the party through rough forests of fir and low-lying brush. Using their axes, they cut a swath up a steep embankment, and across a large high plain where the land was boggy. For miles, they trudged through spongy, soaking fields, covered with coarse bushes. Water pooled around their feet, saturating the light animal-hide footwear which they wore. Once, one of their group fell into a water trap, and the party had to struggle to free him.

Finally, the land sloped gently downward, and Torcas led them through a forest of trees into a glen. The valley was in the shape of a great V. At its base lay two lakes and when eventually they reached a land bridge between these, Torcas pointed to the west. At the end of the valley, above the lakes, a waterfall tumbled and crashed between basalt boulders. Rising above the waterfall were cliffs of great shale deposits. These had been split and eroded by wind, rain and frost, and Midreas saw how huge shale blocks, some larger than a half-dozen of his huts, had broken away from the great stone outcroppings and lay scattered on the valley floor like the playthings of giants.

The group walked silently by the still western lake toward this scattering of monstrous rocks. At last, they stood by the great boulders. Here, Midreas laid his hand on one of the monumental blocks, the sun falling onto his face. Looking at his people he said, "From these we will build the shrine for the scrolls of Psorsis. It will not be an easy task and all of our people will have to put their backs into this work. We shall not finish this citadel in our lifetime. But in my bones, I know that on a spring day such as this, the storehouse of our ancestor's knowledge shall be safe and the scrolls shall rest in the Place of the Sun, secure at last."

Midreas spent over a year devising a method to transport the huge blocks back to the site of the monument. He sent a team of fifty engineers to the shale valley. There, they selected and marked the great stones which would compose the structure of the monument to Psorsis. Then, followed by a team of builders and carpenters, these men cleared the way, forming rough roads through trees and underbrush. The sounds of Atlantean axes echoed through the countryside for many months, stopping only when night made work impossible.

Over the boggy ground, lengths of felled timber were laid, side by side. Thousands of logs were used to cover the soft earth. Other carpenters were assigned the task of building two great barges capable of bearing the weight of the shale slabs. They would also have to withstand the forces of the tides and waves at sea.

Relentlessly, Midreas trekked back and forth from one valley to the other, supervising the work, encouraging his people, providing them with strength and hope for the future.

In late autumn, three years after he first visited the shale valley, he stood there once again, his men around him, waiting for the results of his work to be realised. In front of him lay one of the great blocks. The shale had been roughly squared off. Attached to one end of it was a network of ropes. These ran through a series of wooden pulleys which, in turn, hung from huge wooden timbers. One hundred of his strongest men held the ends of the ropes, waiting for his orders.

Midreas faced them. "For over three years we have

laboured so that we might begin our task. Now, let us start! Men of Atlantis, we work for our future!"

Midreas himself then picked up one of the ropes, pulling with all his considerable strength. The others joined their leader in his task. One hundred men dressed in working hides toiled as they never had before. The work was back-breaking. For a moment, it seemed that they worked in vain because the great block refused to budge. Then, almost imperceptibly at first, the end of the block shifted. Slowly, it moved from its bed where it had lain for centuries, and rose inch by inch into the air. Three feet above the ground, Midreas shouted for them to hold.

"Now! Carpenters! Move to your task!" Twenty carpenters quickly pushed a huge wooden platform beneath the rock. The platform was fitted with fifteen wooden runners, which would disperse the great weight over the ground, and which could move easily over rock, wood or earth. When they had positioned it correctly beneath the block, Midreas commanded his men to lower the slab into position.

Slowly, the rock was lowered. At last, it rested on the platform, the wooden structure sinking slightly into the earth because of the great weight. Midreas inspected their work. "So, the platform bears the weight of the giant stone well. I am pleased with your work, carpenters. Now, we begin the task of moving the stone."

More ropes were attached to the sled. His men again took hold of the ropes, and began the difficult task of pulling the huge weight out of the valley where it had rested for aeons.

Both day and night, the men of Midreas worked at their task. It took them six days to move the shale block out of the valley to face the dangerous journey across the bog. While the wooden path had been well prepared, many of the timber pilings broke or sank beneath the great weight. When this happened, gatherers were sent to the forest. Hours later, they would return with new timber, fitting it snugly into the wooden path.

For forty-seven days, the men of Midreas toiled. Finally,

they brought their huge load onto the beach. The tide rolled in, seeming to greet them not only in welcome but also in challenge. The barges made by the Atlanteans rested in the water, awaiting their trial.

Midreas allowed his men to rest for a day in order to replenish their strength. Then, they were ready. Using wooden pilings and pulleys, they levered the great stone behemoth out across the wet sands toward the barges.

Midreas stood, thigh deep in water, directing his people. "Torcas!" he called to his chief engineer. "The rope is slack! Careful, or we shall lose our treasure to the sea!" Now, the judgement of Midreas and his engineer was tested to its limits. With the barges swinging in the surf of high tide, the great stone was pushed and pulled gently, like a fragile piece of glass, out on to the wooden pilings. It rested level with the surface of the water. When all was ready, Midreas gave his order.

"Sink the barges!" His barges floated not only because they were made of wood, but also because of the hide flotation bags which were attached to their sides. Once inflated, they gave the barges buoyancy. Uninflated, the rock ballast carried at the bottom of the barges pulled them under the surface of the water. At their leader's command, the carpenters let the air out of the flotation bags. Slowly, the barges sank beneath the water.

"Position them quickly! The weight of the rock is great upon the pilings!" Now, the barges were moved between the pilings, under the stone slab. When all was ready, Midreas looked back at men manning his pumps.

"Reinflate!" The portable pumps, turned by hand, pumped air through reed piping into the flotation bags. His men pumped quickly, the sweat rolling down their faces even in the cool breeze. Slowly, the bags filled with air. Torcas watched with concern, looking often at his leader. The bags were almost full, and had refloated the barges. They rested, now, beneath the great shale slab. But still, the rock did not move. "Are you certain that the bags will float the rock?"

Midreas looked at him. "If my calculations are correct, they will float the great rock." He turned to his men at the pumps. "Work harder, my men. We are almost there!"

Torcas ran to his leader's side. "But surely, Midreas, with such pressure the bags will burst."

Midreas replied, "My sister Dorea and her women made those bags. They will withstand the pressure."

Finally, it seemed that the bags would take no more air. The men at the pumps slowed, afraid. "Move aside," Midreas said. "I will make the great stone float on the water."

Midreas took the handle of a pump in his huge hands. His great muscles shining with the sweat of his labour, Midreas moved the pump. Again, and again he turned the handle, and encouraged, his men joined their leader, new strength surging through their arms. Now, they could hear the air course through the reeds, moving out over the water and into the bags.

They watched. Slowly at first, and then more quickly, the stone rose above the water. Finally, both of the barges floated, the giant stone riding on the surface of the sea.

"Now have I shown you, Torcas?" Midreas said. "The stone which will help to protect the scrolls of Psorsis floats on the water. Now we can bring it to our home."

The journey across the open water took two days. The Atlanteans, good seamen, steered their awkward vessel carefully out of the small harbour and began their voyage north along the coast. With Midreas standing at the bow, they navigated carefully around the great island that jutted out from the land. At night, they found shelter, grounding their craft on a sandy beach. The next morning, they started their short journey again. At last, they came to the mouth of their river. Turning inland, they rowed up the current until they came to the great bend in the river. There, they saw the people standing waist-high in water, waving and cheering in welcome.

Midreas smiled. He placed his arm on the shoulder of Torcas. They had brought the first great stone home to its new resting place.

8

Newgrange is situated in a green field, in a flat area of grasses and hedgerows seemingly carved out of the side of a hill. The area has been kept relatively free from modern influence. Farms lie like patchwork around the site.

Newgrange is a megalithic burial site. Archaeologists believe that it was built 5000 years ago – well before Egypt's pyramids. It is therefore one of the world's oldest structural sites.

The ride up to Newgrange was easy. Jonathan and Cathy pedalled smoothly on roads lined with blackthorn and privet. Blackberry bushes bloomed in the early afternoon sun. It was hardly a day for calamity.

They rode down a long road. Jonathan was in the lead, Cathy pedalling hard to keep up. "You're sure it's down here?" She had to yell into the wind.

"Told you. I come up here all the time."

"Where is it, then? I don't see any sign of it."

"Almost there. Just around the bend."

The two cyclists took the curve, and Cathy slowed, then stopped. Jonathan looked back and saw her peering over the hedge. He turned around, and came back to her. Together, they looked at the monument of Newgrange.

"Pretty impressive, isn't it?"

In front of them, Newgrange rose from the surrounding fields. It was a half mile away, yet its size dwarfed them, immense even at that distance.

Jonathan and Cathy gazed at its greatness. Created in

gigantic proportions, it also had a certain elegance. The green grass which covered its top and sides contrasted vividly with its white stonework. This white quartz, fixed to the front of the monument, glistened in the sunlight. Dark grey standing stones stood as silent testimonials to the people who had engineered its creation.

From their position, they could see tourists wandering around the grounds in front of the monument. The sheer magnitude of Newgrange transformed the visitors into tiny insects of no consequence.

"I'd forgotten how big it was."

Jonathan looked at her. "How long is it since you were here?"

"I don't know. Maybe five years."

He smiled. "You're in for a treat. Come on. Let's get closer." They mounted their bikes, cycling along the road, dappled in sunlight. "Hold on!" Jonathan stopped his bike suddenly. He glanced back at Cathy. "Do you see what I see?"

She looked in the direction that he was pointing. The old black Morris Minor was parked in the visitors' car park. Barnabus, himself, stood at the wire fence that surrounded Newgrange, lost in thought.

"Let's park the bikes out of sight. We'll take a look at what he's doing."

Cathy frowned. "You're not suggesting that we spy on him, are you?"

He looked at her. "Sure. How else do you think we're going to find out what he's up to? Come on. Let's get going."

They hid the bikes carefully in the blackthorn and made their way down the road. Tourists meandered about their parked cars and some crossed the street to the tourist office. The two students made their way through the crowd, trying to keep Barnabus in sight. He no longer stood at the fence. For a second, they thought that they had lost him. But then Cathy saw him standing at the entrance to the monument.

"You keep an eye on him. I'm going to check the car." Jonathan crossed quickly to the Morris. The bags which

Barnabus had thrown in earlier were gone. He walked back to Cathy. "He's dumped his stuff already. The car's empty."

"He's going in through the entrance. See him?" She pointed. Jonathan nodded.

"Why don't we just stand here and see what he's up to?"

"You don't think we should go in?"

He shook his head. "We'd scare him off. He doesn't want us about, for whatever reason. Let's just watch from here."

The two stood at the wire fence, keeping their teacher in view. First, he made his way over toward the entrance to the monument. A tour guide was trying to gather her charges into a manageable group. Twenty or thirty people loafed around, waiting for the lecture to start. Barnabus stood at the back of the group. Waiting.

At last the woman started her lecture. Jonathan and Cathy stood fifty or sixty yards away from them, and couldn't hear any details. They saw her pointing, though. She took in the great magnitude of the megalithic structure, the standing stones, lying silently, as if in wait. She pointed to the bend in the Boyne river that flowed by and at the quartz of the monument. Finally, she traced the whorl-shaped designs of the kerb stone, which stood guard to the entrance. She talked for ten or fifteen minutes, then motioned to the crowd.

"She'll take them inside, now," Jonathan said. "They'll go in and she'll show what happens at the winter solstice."

"How's that?" said Cathy.

"It's no big deal, really. Once the crowd is inside, they dim all the lights. Then they turn on a light display. It shows the sun coming up over the horizon – just as it does on the shortest day of the year. The beam of sunlight shines through the entrance and all the way to the back of the chamber. The experts think that this is how the ancient Irish honoured their dead. They say that in ancient times, the bodies of their leaders were cremated at the centre of the monument. The light of the sun, on the shortest day of the year, signifies a rebirth – or something like that. Actually, it's quite a feat of engineering."

"I guess it would have been, considering that they didn't

have any really modern technology or anything."

Jonathan turned his attention back to the monument. "The crowd is moving in. Let's try to keep tabs on Barnabus."

"How long will they be in there?"

"Oh, I don't know. Not more than five or ten minutes."

They watched Barnabus enter the monument along with the other tourists. He kept to the back of the group, stopping for a moment to study the great carved kerbstone.

Jonathan and Cathy waited patiently by the fence. At last, the crowd started to reappear. "So, showtime is over. Let's see what he does next." They waited for Barnabus to re-emerge. The crowd walked aimlessly from the entrance. Some stood by the kerbstone, others walked over to examine the standing stones. Many chose to walk back toward the entrance. They waited but no Barnabus appeared. At last the guide came out into the sunlight. Cathy looked earnestly at Jonathan. "He must still be in there, examining something."

"Let's hold on for a couple of minutes."

They waited, but still no Barnabus. "Maybe we missed him. I'm going into the monument. Cathy, why don't you walk down to see if he's over by the standing stones? I'll see if he came out. Meet you at the entrance."

"Right."

Cathy took her time as she walked back along the fencing. Most of the tourists had left but some lingered in the warm sunshine, touching the standing stones or looking out on the view of the Boyne. No Barnabus.

She came back to meet Jonathan. He stood in thought. "Can't find him?"

She motioned behind her. "He wasn't back there."

"And he isn't up here. That's really strange." The guide came toward them. She looked tired. "Excuse me." Jonathan walked up to her. "I was supposed to meet our teacher here. He might have gone in with the previous group. He's small, quite old. He has a moustache and wears glasses. I just wondered if you might have seen him."

She looked at him, in thought. "Let's see. Yes, I think there was a man like that in the last group. As far as I remember, he came into the monument with me. You say you were supposed to meet him?"

"That's right."

She shrugged. "Well, if he went in, he has to come out. You can't get lost in Newgrange. There's only one entrance, and once you're in, there's only the corridor."

"No other exits?" Jonathan asked. "I've been in and I don't remember other passages."

"That's right. Just the one passage. So if he came in with us, he has to be around." She looked at him. "Anyway, I was the last one out, and there wasn't anyone left behind. I hope you find him."

"Thanks."

He took Cathy by the arm, pulling her back up the road. "Come on. We've got to get moving."

She was having trouble keeping up. "Where to?"

"I don't know. But somehow, Barnabus managed to stay in there." He stopped suddenly, looking at the monument. "Right now, somewhere in that pile of stone, our teacher is unlocking a puzzle. And we're going to have to figure out a way of finding him."

Working back from the entrance to Newgrange, Jonathan and Cathy looked for other paths which might let them approach the structure. The main road was lined with a continuous hedge. Certainly, Barnabus would be unable to drive the Morris Minor through the hedge. "What he needed was a way in. A road, or a path . . . "

Cathy thought hard. "I thought I saw an old track or something."

"Where?"

"About a half-mile back up the road."

Jonathan and Cathy pedalled hard back up the small hill. Newgrange was on their left, hidden by the hedges. The road turned and twisted, and at last, they came to a small section where the hedgerows disappeared. Through a small cluster of beech trees, they could see the monument rising above its green foundation.

"Here!"

Cathy had stopped by an old iron fence. Rusted from disuse, and broken in a number of places, a piece of barbed wire hung between two gate-posts in a weak attempt to prevent unwelcome entry. An old grass path led from the gate, away from the main road, towards a group of trees and low scrub behind Newgrange.

"See? Look at the fresh tyre tracks. A car has been down here recently."

Jonathan nodded. "Seems about right." He looked at Cathy. "Well, we might as well take a look. Let's leave the bikes here."

They laid their bikes in the grass, and started walking down the path. It was obvious to them that the rough road was no longer used. Great swarms of midges played beneath the trees, and they could see rabbits sitting along the verge of the path. An old house stood beneath an umbrella of oak trees and creepers. They walked past as the path grew ever more tangled. They could still make out the rough tracks of the car.

The path seemed to come to a dead end in a thicket of twisted briar and felled saplings. Jonathan made his way carefully along the periphery, walking along the ruts made by the car wheels. At last, he stopped and looked around for Cathy. "This is it. See? Here's where he went through." He pointed. The thicket had been cut. They could see a field through the tangled, torn vegetation. Jonathan started his way into it. "We've come about far enough, I'd say. I'm no great judge of distances, but I'll bet that just on the other side of this is . . . "

Cathy stepped warily along the rough path. "Is what, Jonathan?" She caught up to him finally, standing at his shoulder. In front of them, a hundred yards away, stood the ancient monument.

He smiled. "Newgrange."

They found Barnabus's supplies piled neatly against a small wall. The briefcase, suitcase, computer – everything that he had packed was there. Jonathan stood, puzzled, looking at the things.

"Well? Don't just stand there, Jonathan. You've been so sure of yourself. Why has he left them here?" Cathy glared at him. "You've brought me miles from the house, out to God knows where, and we only find his supplies. And at the back of Newgrange, of all places! There isn't even an entrance back here! And where is Barnabus? Answer me that!"

"Give me a second, will you? Anyway, you're the maths wizard. You think of something."

"Oh, that's great. Now you want me to do it all. Might I remind you that we've been away from school all day. Our parents are bound to have noticed by now. They probably have the guards out after us. That's great news! They're probably not only looking for a crazy teacher, but for two of his stupid students as well."

"Just give me a minute, will you!"

She stood silently, glaring at him.

"Look, let's just think about what we do know. You're the analytical genius. Stop whining and help me for a change. All right?"

She relented. "All right, but make it quick."

Jonathan started to pace. "OK. We know that Barnabus came to Newgrange. His car is parked in front of the monument. Right?"

"Agreed."

"And we know he left his belongings here. His suitcase and stuff. Right?"

"Elementary, my dear Watson. You have any more great insights?"

"Hold the cynicism for the classroom," he replied. "Now, we also know that he went into the monument. *And he did not come out*. True?"

"Maybe."

He turned to her abruptly. "Oh, come on. You saw him go into Newgrange. Did you see him come out or not?"

She thought for a minute. "Not."

"So we're agreed that he's still in there somewhere."

She nodded. "Well, if he didn't come out, he must still be in there."

"Right." Jonathan considered. "Now the question is, why did he leave his things here? I mean, he could have left them in the car . . . Or he could have left them close by the entrance so that he could get to them quickly. Not back here, so far away." He paused. "Unless . . . "

"Unless what, Jonathan?"

He turned to her, excited. "Cathy, think back to the house. To the model of Newgrange. Do you remember it?"

"Do talk sense, Jonathan. Of course I remember it."

"Think of the monument. Remember? There was another entrance. A rear entrance."

She thought. "That's right. Of course! But you said that there wasn't another entrance."

"No, I said that I didn't *think* there was another entrance. But Barnabus did. So there must be one. Don't just stand there. Come on!"

They started scrambling up the hill, through a stand of hedgerow, up to the back of the monument. "Where do we start?"

"Over here. Let's try this kerbstone." They studied the huge carved square of shale intently. Its design of whorls and triangles refused to divulge any secrets. Cathy stood up despondently. "Nothing here. Where next?"

Jonathan looked over the monument. Steps led up to a path which worked its way around the site. "I'm going to try this side. Maybe you can work your way back down the hill." He started walking up the footpath, studying the stones that lined the mound.

Cathy shook her head, yelling at him. "That's fine. I'll look. But I don't think we're going to find anything."

He stopped in his tracks, turning slowly to her. "Would you try to be positive for once? Just once?" He turned again, muttering. She could just hear him. "Some things just don't change. Damn!"

The sun was starting to set and the long rays of light made it more difficult for them to see. For over an hour they searched for the rear entrance. Once Jonathan thought that he found a depression in the monument and he called for Cathy. They searched, but they found no seams, nothing to indicate that a door or trap was located underneath. Finally, she called to him.

"Jonathan, come on down." He climbed down from where he had been searching, to find her sitting on the pile of Barnabus's belongings. "Find anything?"

"Nothing."

"That's it then. I tried, and we didn't find anything. Now it's getting late. My folks will be worried about me. And we still have the bike ride home."

"Yeah." He sat down abruptly beside her. "OK. I don't know where else to look. It's around here. I know it."

She smiled slightly. "If nothing else, Jonathan, you're persistent. Thick, maybe. But persistent." She looked at him. He sat with his head in his hands. "Look, if it's any help, we'll come back tomorrow and pick up where we left off. Goodness knows why I'm saying this. I really don't think there's anything here. But we'll try again."

"Thanks. It's great to know you've got such confidence in me."

"Some sleuth." She laughed. "Next time, bring your magnifying glass." She got up, standing over him. "What do we do about his things?"

He looked at the pile of Barnabus's belongings. "I don't know. I guess I'll bring the computer home. But we might as well leave the other stuff here. I can't say that a night outside will do them much damage." He got up, standing beside her. In the dim twilight, he was acutely conscious of the way Newgrange towered above him like a mystic mountain. "It's strange, isn't it, this place. I can almost feel the ghosts of the ancients. The people who built this. They must have been amazing people."

Cathy smiled weakly in the darkness. "Let's leave talk of ghosts for the daytime. Come on. I'd like to start back."

"Sure. Be careful going back through that scrub." He moved to put his hand on her shoulder, then thought better of it. I guess she can pretty well look after herself, he thought.

It was then that he felt it. At first, it was just a prickling; a sensation that moved over his skin. It moved the hair on his arms and head, and he thought that a breeze must be getting up. He looked up. The leaves on the trees hung motionless in the still evening air .

"Jonathan?" He turned, and saw Cathy standing, looking back through the bushes, shocked. He looked back towards the mound. The hill stood as it had for thousands of years. But as he looked he saw it move. Change. The air seemed to dance. Currents of electricity glided back and forth in front of them, and the whole hillside seemed to turn inside out. For a moment, Jonathan thought that he could see directly into the bowels of the earth. What he saw frightened him. Great rivers of water spun and swung, tumbling through great conduits, leaping and foaming in their voyage toward an unknown sea. Below, a gigantic fire burned in great molten fissures, blinding in their intensity, so bright that they burned in blues and pinks and purples and intense reds. Columns of light, of liquid rock, the very soul of the planet, tumbled together, growing in intensity; a giant head of molten earth grew towards them, meeting beneath the rocks that had stood quiet for so many aeons.

The ground shook slightly. He put out his hand and found Cathy's. They stood watching, too frightened to run. Not thinking. Only watching. The rivers of molten earth and rushing waters converged beneath them. The light blinded them and they put their hands instinctively to their eyes. The ground shook again and they fell to their knees. Above them, a great pillar of intense light soared from the very rock of the monument, up into the twilight, past the rising moon, and into the vast spaces of the universe.

At last, Jonathan opened his eyes. In front of him was a door. Just as on the model. A door with lintels carved in whorls and circles, complete and perfect. And standing in the centre of the door was Barnabus.

9

In his remaining years, Midreas accomplished many things. His goal was simple: to preserve his people from cultural extinction. With his engineers, farmers and gatherers, Midreas worked so that the village founded in the Place of the Sun grew and prospered. No longer did his people fear death from starvation. He organised them into units of specialists; they hunted, fished, and grew crops which were shared by all the people.

To his eye, the village was still primitive. Simple wood huts housed the once-proud Atlanteans, and Midreas knew that they had lost – at least for the present – the prosperity which they had once known. At sunset, his sister Dorea – now a leader in her own right – would often find him wandering by the river, thinking of what had been.

"As Atlanteans, we conquered our world. Now, we are humbled, and we must accept that we are as we are." She knew that he thought back to their great cities and technology, and then compared these to the simple way of life which they had been forced to adopt. She did her best to comfort him.

"You have saved our people from extinction. Because of your leadership, the people of Atlantis survive. One day, we shall rise to heights of which our father never dreamed."

He took comfort from her words. He knew that she was right. And he looked, then, up at the great mound which was starting to take shape on the field above their valley.

Of all of the projects upon which Midreas worked, the shrine for the scrolls of Psorsis gave him the most pleasure, the most hope for the future. Throughout the years, his most talented workers strove to accomplish his dream. Slowly the great structure took shape.

He had spent many hours with his most trusted engineers designing the work. With the great stones of slate arriving weekly from the shale valley to the south, Midreas spent days, weeks and months in positioning each one precisely. With his most psychic people he walked every part of the field, sensing, as only an Atlantean could, the great powers of water, magma and magnetic fields which lay beneath the surface of the earth. His engineers marked these centres of force with great stones. These points of potential energy would provide the monument with its as yet undeveloped power.

Work began early each morning with the summoning of the scientists and mathematicians. Working with great accuracy, they mapped the place illumined by the first rays of the sun. One morning, in the dead of winter, the sun appeared in its most southerly position, and Midreas marked the point with a rock.

Rising from the stone, he faced his people. "Here," he said, "is where the sun rises to bring light into the darkness. The entrance to the monument shall be here. In this way, we shall show future generations that the wisdom of Psorsis will once again bring the light of knowledge to our people."

Midreas ordered his engineers to dig a great chamber at the centre of the monument. Into this tomb, they lowered the scrolls of Psorsis, still housed in their wooden and glass vessel. Over this, they built a wall of rock, protecting the scrolls from the elements until such time as his people could fathom their secrets.

On the day of the entombment, Midreas was approached by a delegation. He had heard that some of his people were discontent, longing for their old way of life; for the riches and ease of living which the Atlanteans had once enjoyed. This group desired that the scrolls be opened immediately. An old mathematician, Pythmeas, spoke for this group. Now as head of the delegation, he approached Midreas.

"Leader," Pythmeas began, "we see how you intend to entomb the scrolls of Psorsis. Surely, I will not live to see them opened. Nor will you. Not, that is, if we follow your way. I ask you to consider this: I knew your father, Psorsis, well. I knew his genius. I studied with him." Pythmeas looked back to his delegation with pride. "It was said that in my youth I was as bright and as knowledgeable as he. I ask you, Midreas, why leave the secrets of these scrolls to future generations? Should we not attempt to unlock their secrets now?" The men in the delegation murmured in agreement, and Pythmeas grew bolder. His voice rose.

"We have followed your way for many years, now. And what have you done? Yes," he nodded his head disparagingly to Midreas, "I will give you credit for saving us. You led us from our land, ravaged as it was by the Borgnoff, the Destroyer star. You protected our people and our culture from certain extinction. But now, look at what you have brought us to." Pythmeas swept his hand toward the humble dwellings in the valley below them. "Where is the tremendous culture that was once the Atlantean people? Where are our great buildings? Our art? Our technology? Our way of life?"

He pointed at Midreas and spoke with rising passion. "You have saved us only to allow us to perish!" His voice grew harsh. "Is this what the people of Atlantis have been reduced to? Crude mud huts?" He flicked at his worn hides. "The clothes of an animal? Food not fit for consumption by man?" He turned to the delegation for support.

"The scrolls of Psorsis contain knowledge which will allow us to become great once more! Why do you not let us open them now? Are you hiding something, Midreas?" Pythmeas's voice grew quieter, gently taunting. "Is there some secret which you wish to keep hidden away? Some power from your dead father which you desire only for yourself? Why will you not share this knowledge now, and let our people rise again?"

The men shouted in agreement. Pythmeas stood before his leader, gaining confidence. "If that is your aim, then I say that we should take the scrolls of Psorsis for ourselves! By force, if you dare to stop us. These men and I – we shall read what was left to us by your dead father! With that knowledge, we shall regain the greatness that was once Atlantis!"

The men in the group roared their approval.

Slowly, Midreas put his hands in the air, quietening the group. Rising to his full height, he glared at the men with contempt. Then, his eyes softened, and he reached out, placing his hand gently on the shoulder of Pythmeas.

"Is this how you approach your leader now, Pythmeas," he said softly, "With threats?" His eyes searched the face of Pythmeas. He turned, addressing the rest of the men. "Is this how we have survived? By warring with each other? Has not our survival been based on the common concern which each of us has for the other?"

"You, Mortis." He addressed an old man standing at the front of the group. "When you broke your leg, did the people not feed you and your family while you recovered?" He picked out a youth. "And Tinian. When your parents died, did my sister Dorea not foster you with her own hands and heart? And Rathmola . . . " He turned his attention to a middle-aged man. "I knew your father well. What would he think if he knew that you turned your back on your heritage?"

Midreas let his hand drop, and he turned from them, looking down into the valley below them. "I am as frustrated and as angry at our fate as you are. Look at what we have become." His voice dropped. "We are but a shadow of our former selves. No longer do we rule our world. No longer do we enjoy prosperity. No longer do our minds probe the limitless possibilities that come with knowledge. Yet we survive. Daily, our lives improve. Some day, we will again have time for study. For contemplation. For thought. But not now!" He turned to Pythmeas. "I pity you, old man. See what you have become. Your pride prevents you from seeing things clearly! Do you really think that you can understand the great works of Psorsis?" Midreas laughed lightly. "Even Psorsis himself did not understand it entirely. He did not know the full potential of that knowledge. Nor did he have time to assimilate it fully. Instead, he allowed himself to perish! Along with the rest of our people." He turned, sadly. "No, Pythmeas. Today, we do not have the resources to interpret the scrolls. Someday, the people of Atlantis will! Until then, we shall do as my father asked. We shall keep them safe for our children and our children's children. That is my decision."

Midreas looked deep into the eyes of the old man. Pythmeas stood for a moment, studying the determined set jaw of his leader, a man of his own physical size and strength. Slowly, the challenge in his eyes died.

"You shall see, Midreas," he muttered. "Some day, one of us shall challenge you for leadership."

"Yes, old man. And on that day, we shall be ruined by fools. Go, now. Take your women – " his eyes swept toward the group " – and get back to your huts."

The men of Pythmeas stood for a moment in confusion. Then they dispersed, leaving Midreas with his own thoughts. For the present, their challenge had been beaten. But some day . . . some day other men might shatter the fragile balance of his leadership and tear their world apart. Midreas sighed deeply, and turned back to the monument. Never again would he take his position of authority – or their continuing survival – for granted.

Slowly but surely, the great edifice continued to rise into the air. In order to tackle some of the more complex building problems, the engineers developed a block and tackle system which could shift the great rocks with little trouble. Using levers and a fulcrum, they were able to move the blocks into exact positions, aligning them into their required patterns.

Little occupied Midreas now but the construction of the monument. As he grew older, he grew more content. But still, he could not rule out the possibility that others within his small community might some day challenge his leadership. If that happened, all might be lost.

Midreas also came to know a sad truth. He realised that the Atlanteans would never rise to their former greatness – not in his lifetime and not without the aid of the scrolls. But these now lay protected beneath a rising shield of rock, and Midreas was content that they would be there for future generations.

In the fifty-third year of his life, Midreas finally took himself a wife, Cathelonia. She was beautiful and wise, and well able to put up with her husband's moods. At the end of the first year of their marriage, Cathelonia gave birth to a son, Marthras. On the morning after the birth, Midreas walked up the valley, carrying his newborn child in his arms. As the sun broke over the horizon, Midreas held his son aloft and said, "Now, it is up to you to protect the civilisation that was once Atlantis. To you, I entrust the care of my people. To you, my son, I leave our destiny. To you, I entrust the care of the scrolls of your grandfather, Psorsis." He held the baby to his breast. "And I shall do everything that I can to see that you shall become the new leader." Midreas gazed at his son and saw therein his own immortality. With that knowledge he felt complete.

Four years later, Midreas fell while working on the monument, causing his leg to fracture, the bone breaking through the skin. He lost much blood. By the time his tribesmen had carried him back to his hut, the old leader's face was ashen, and they could see that his end was near. "Run," they said. "Fetch the elders and the mathematicians and the engineers that they might see his end."

Cathelonia cradled him in her arms, and his son Marthras stood nearby. At his side also stood Dorea, his sister. And, with the other leaders of his society around him, Midreas spoke quickly, knowing that his strength would leave him soon. "Hear me," he said. "I know that my end is near. Hear me, and do my bidding, while I am still your leader." Midreas gasped a little with pain. "Know that survival of the Atlanteans does not rest in your strength or even in your industry. It rests in your hearts, and in your courage. Know, too, that the future of Atlantis rests in the knowledge contained in the scrolls of Psorsis – the scrolls which we have spent a life-time protecting. Hear me, Torcas." The old engineer shuffled closer to him.

"On my deathbed, I charge you to finish the monument. With this completed, the scrolls will be protected. Future generations will marvel at its construction, and wonder at its purpose. But we shall know, will we not, Torcas?"

The engineer shifted slightly. "Yes, Midreas."

"The monument shall be a shield, protecting that which will bring bounty to Atlanteans! I charge you to protect the scrolls for the rest of your days, and thereafter, to hand on this trust to the next keeper of the scrolls!"

Torcas breathed deeply. "It shall be done, Midreas."

The leader paused for a minute. His breath came in small gasps. Time was running out. "Now, as to my successor. We are not an uncivilised race. We do not rule by force but by agreement. You all have the right to choose a new leader as you see fit. But I ask you to consider this." He cast his eyes around, and they fell for a moment on Pythmeas, the old man who had once challenged his authority.

"Remember. In disagreement lies discord. And in discord lies the potential for destruction! If you cannot all agree on a new leader, our society will fracture, like a great rock split asunder by the earthquake. And in fragmenting, you will not survive.

"Therefore, I ask you to consider my son, Marthras. He is too young, yet, to lead. But I ask you, Cathelonia, as his mother, and you, Dorea, as my sister, to lead on his behalf and to tutor him until he is fit to lead on his own. And you, Pythmeas," he gazed at the old man, "you who challenged me years ago, I ask you too to help these women in their task. By this means, unity will blossom. This is my will." He gazed at the people surrounding him, reaching out finally to touch his son, Marthras, on the shoulder. Now, Midreas could only whisper, and only those close to him heard as he uttered, "This is my will, Marthras. It is my will that our culture shall survive and grow again. I may never again be with you in body but I shall always be with you in spirit. Tell this to our people. Ask them for their agreement. If they know that I have asked, they shall agree, because they know that I have always worked toward their best interests: the survival of Atlanteans."

Then, Midreas closed his eyes, and was gone.

That night, a great fire was built. On this pyre, the body of Midreas was placed. When the fire had burned to ash, his family reverently collected the remains, and placed them in a fired clay jar. Then the entire settlement formed a procession as they took the remains of Midreas up the valley, placing them in the exact centre of the monument. They left them there knowing that on the shortest day of the year, the sun would shine on them, as Midreas had planned, as a sign of new life.

Now, it was left to Marthras to protect the scrolls. Midreas had done all that he could.

10

The great light disappeared as suddenly as it had come. Now, Jonathan and Cathy heard only the gentle rush of the swallows as they moved through the evening air. For a moment, they thought that it had all been a dream – that the great pillars of light and the rushing, tumbling waters had been in their imagination. Jonathan looked back towards the great mound. It was normal again. The glistening forces of electricity were gone. He shook his head slowly and turned to Cathy.

"Did you see what I saw?"

She looked up at Newgrange. "Don't look now, but it's still there." He looked up. Barnabus walked down the side of the mound, toward them.

"Hey. It's him. It's really him!"

"Hello!" he called to them, his coat flapping madly as he made his way over rocks and clumps of ground. "You followed me! I'm delighted!"

"Well, we found him," Cathy said.

"I'm not so sure that I'm glad we did."

Their teacher came up to them. "Curious, were you? Couldn't leave me to go it alone? Well, now that you've found me, you might as well give me a hand. Here. Pick these things up." He started lifting the luggage off the ground. Jonathan stood watching in amazement.

"Barnabus. Did you see that?"

"See what?" he asked.

"The light! Didn't you see it at all?"

The teacher stopped, and looked at him keenly. "I was on the inside, if you'll remember, Jonathan. Tell me what you saw."

"I don't know! It was fantastic. First, I felt all prickly. Like some sort of electricity was running through me."

Barnabus considered this. "That would be the magnetic field. Yes. Go on."

"Then, I don't know what I saw." Jonathan turned back towards the monument, gesturing as he went. "There was this huge river. Sort of a whirlpool. It was all crashing and tumbling – going mad. Then there was this sort of great bright light. Rivers of red. Like lava flowing. All of it moving up towards the water."

"Yes, that makes sense," Barnabus answered coolly. "It was lava."

"And then they combined. And this huge light! It just bolted out of the side of the hill. Right up and out. Heaven only knows where it went."

Barnabus smiled. "Yes. That was the energy beam. I've seen that work." He stood, musing.

"But what was it?"

"Hhmm? Oh, well, don't you see, you just saw a power source, that's all. Come on, pick up this stuff, and follow me. I'll show it to you."

Barnabus, suitcase in hand, started back up the hill. Cathy looked at Jonathan. "You heard him. Grab some stuff, and let's see."

Hurriedly they picked up the few articles which were left, and followed Barnabus. The side of the monument appeared to be untouched. As if nothing had happened. Then they were at the door.

The frame of this back entrance looked new. Square, and larger than the front portal, the door was framed with huge uprights, seemingly freshly cut. Great whorls were carved into the surfaces and Barnabus paused to touch them. "For years, archaeologists have tried to understand their meaning," he said, tracing the carvings with his fingers. "Some thought that they represented the sun. Some said that they meant water. Others even held that they were the signs of comets." He laughed slightly. "Little did they know that they were all, in their own way, correct." He looked back at his students. "Come," he said simply. "I'll show you now."

Carefully, he led them into the side of the mound. At first, Jonathan thought that they would somehow enter the main chamber, but then they started to descend. The path which they took seemed steep, and he had trouble keeping his footing. What puzzled him most, though, was the light. The path which they travelled was lit dimly. Yet, Jonathan did not see any source of light. Cathy noticed, too.

"Why isn't it pitch black in here?"

He was following her, with Barnabus in the lead. "I don't know. Electrical, perhaps."

Barnabus replied from the front. "No. Magnetic. My guess is that the magnetic field in this area excites the very atomic structure of the rocks. What we're seeing is the light given off by their energy."

"But no one noticed a magnetic field in Newgrange before."

Barnabus stopped and turned to them, smiling in the dimness. "That is so, Cathy. Apparently, it is shielded. It exists only here. Not outside the mound. Not in the other chamber. Only here." He turned. "Not much further, now. I'll explain in a minute."

Ahead of them, they could make out what seemed to be the end of the tunnel. The path started to level off, and it grew brighter. Then, they entered a great vault. They stood, straining to see in the dim light.

The room was as large as the monument itself. On the walls, a rock tapestry of whorls glowed in a multicoloured hue. To their eyes, they seemed to shift and move: now solid, now translucent, almost ethereal. "Electrical aberration," Barnabus said softly. "That accounts for the light, and for the shifting." The room was practically empty. They walked further into it. The ceiling seemed to disappear above them, into the shadows. Straining, they could make out sparks of light above them.

71

"Like starlight," Cathy said.

Barnabus smiled. "It is, rather, isn't it? Actually, it's quartz. The facets of the rock are reflecting the light back to us. But you're very close to the real answer." They walked on.

Suddenly, Jonathan stopped. "Look!" He was staring down at his feet.

The rock floor seemed to end. Now, even though they walked on a solid surface, they seemed suspended in mid-air. As if walking on glass or the surface of a clear lake. Below them were the images which Jonathan and Cathy had seen before. Great cataracts of water spiralled and crashed between giant stones, gushing and churning from one wall of granite to another, sending up plumes of spray. The water reflected colours, and in one place, a rainbow hung suspended in a cloud of moisture.

The colours were created by a blast-furnace of heat and energy. Barnabus pointed down into the depths, his face coloured red by the conflagration. "Behold," he said solemnly. "Behold the earth's engine."

"What is it?"

He turned to Cathy. "I should have thought that my prize pupil would be more intuitive. You're seeing the molten energy of the earth's core." They stood, looking. Rivers of molten rock moved sinuously between great lakes of lava. Hot gasses burned lazily, climbing up toward the waters before finally dying. It was a view of hell. Something from Dante's *Inferno*. Standing nervously on the clear surface, they looked into the depths of the earth. "What you are seeing has never before been seen by modern man. Only the ancients understood. They recognised the power that lay waiting. Power beyond even our imagination. Simple forces. Basic forces of ancient elements. I marvel at their genius." Barnabus glanced up. "Come," he said. " I'll show you more."

They approached a dais which rose in the exact centre of the room. It seemed to be made entirely of one quartz crystal. Immense. Its sides were carved with the same whorls that decorated the rest of Newgrange. The top was flat. On it rested a vessel of rough metal, broken and weathered with time. Its surfaces were also decorated. To the side of the dais, assorted materials lay scattered. Most of it was electrical equipment, and Jonathan guessed that this must be the project that Barnabus had worked on in his barn. Their teacher approached the dais.

"Now," he said. "I will show you something." Slowly, he mounted the platform, standing in an oval area which lay next to the metal vessel. The light in the room began to dim. Then, the energy which lay below them grew darker, and the ground around them took on a more solid shape.

As they watched, the dais itself started to glow. Brighter and brighter, the quartz took on its own translucence. Too bright to look at. It lit the chamber. Barnabus, standing on top, pointed suddenly into the air. "Look!"

Above them, the ceiling glowed with the countless stars of the universe. And in the east, the moon rose.

11

The mantle of Midreas's leadership thrown upon the young shoulders of Marthras proved to be heavy. Some Atlanteans felt the loss of Midreas keenly, and were uncertain that the young boy, even with the aid of his trustees, could maintain the reins of leadership. Throughout the village, people whispered that the village would soon know hunger and that death would surely triumph. Most chose to follow the successor, but others were unsure.

Now, Pythmeas saw his opportunity. Quietly at first, he spoke to those willing to listen. He sowed the seeds of discontent and often he drew attention to the primitive conditions in which they lived. To Pythmeas there was but one answer: the opening of the scrolls of Psorsis. With this knowledge, he and he alone would be able to lead the Atlanteans back to their former greatness.

Some were swayed by the elder's argument. Gradually at first, some men turned their backs on young Marthras and quietly looked toward Pythmeas for leadership. But the old man was clever. He never directly challenged Marthras for leadership. Instead, he bided his time, knowing that the day would come when he would control all.

Cathelonia and Dorea did their best to protect Marthras, and, ignoring Pythmeas entirely, set out to carry out the objectives of Midreas. While the dead leader had appointed Pythmeas as one of the child's advisors, the women kept the old man away from the young leader, knowing that the old man might influence the boy wrongly.

In these unquiet years, the boy matured. While it was his intention to carry out the wishes of his father and while he tried to provide for his fellow citizens, Marthras showed little strength as a leader. Often, he heard whisperings among the people. He noted the poverty in which they lived, and listened keenly to stories which the old people told: stories of the great cities of Atlantis, of its riches and power. And as he listened, Marthras grew dissatisfied.

Dorea watched the dissatisfaction that grew within the boy's mind. Often, she and Cathelonia talked for many hours, organising the farmers for new harvests or planning the forays to replenish their food store. Through their industry, they kept the community together, but barely so. Dorea knew that, slowly, Pythmeas was swaying the hearts of the people. And Marthras, as leader, was powerless to stop him.

For a few years, the village continued to thrive. But under Marthras's weak leadership, the people soon grew dissatisfied. The result was a series of petty arguments between the citizens, hoarding of food and lack of co-operation between them. Because of this, the people of the Place of the Sun soon suffered. Gatherers and farmers worked only for themselves, refusing to share their bounty with their fellow citizens unless barter was arranged.

One year, the crops failed entirely. The lessons of their heritage forgotten, and thinking only of themselves, the villagers ignored the perilous situation. In that year a father, watching his young children slowly die of starvation, murdered his neighbour for food. Murder had been unknown to the Atlanteans for countless generations. Not knowing what to do, the people did nothing. Instead, they watched while their civilisation disintegrated around them.

Lawlessness broke out. The once great people warred among themselves. Neighbour attacked neighbour. Brother killed brother. No longer did they choose to follow the Midrean doctrine of community living. Instead, individual force became the rule of the day.

Now, Pythmeas saw his chance. Secretly, he talked with

Marthras, now a young man. Again and again, he pointed out the dark times that had befallen the citizens. He preached the new gospel to Marthras: that their only hope lay in the knowledge buried in the scrolls. As leader, Marthras could order that the shrine of the scrolls be opened. And by doing so, he would not only save his people – no – he would be responsible for restoring the Atlantean culture to its former greatness.

Marthras listened to the old man, and believed. Now eighteen, he felt that he no longer needed advisers. He told his mother and Dorea of his intention to lead on his own and of his decision to control the keeping of the scrolls. The women dissented, knowing that the people were not ready for the knowledge which they contained.

Then something happened which changed the course of their history and brought a time of darkness upon the people. Cathelonia grew sick and two months later was dead. Marthras, seeing this, blamed Dorea. He believed that, had the scrolls been opened, his mother would have been saved. Misguided by grief, he thought that it was through Dorea's negligence that his mother suffered and that his people suffered.

With anger in his heart, Marthras finally turned from his mentors, and pledged his loyalty to Pythmeas. Together, he said, they would rule the people. Together, they would rebuild Atlantis.

Dorea, seeing this, knew that she must take swift action if she were to survive. She enlisted the aid of Rengal, a strong warrior. With him, she addressed the people, telling them that to follow the leadership of Pythmeas and Marthras would bring total destruction. Many of the people refused to believe her. But many also appreciated her wisdom and chose to follow her. That which Midreas feared most had now come to pass. The society which he had nurtured for so long fractured. Father sided against son. Brother fought with brother.

With Rengal aiding her, Dorea moved the group of loyal Atlanteans to the field above the valley. Her motive was clear:

the scrolls of her dead father must be protected. Organising her engineers, she constructed a defensive structure, and made plans to outlast this time of darkness.

While Dorea provided the wisdom which her people needed, Rengal provided the protection. The art of war had long been lost to the Atlantean people. They simply had no need of it. In Rengal they again found the military acumen which their forefathers had developed when establishing their domain aeons earlier. To Rengal, the band of murderers and thieves that threatened them were traitors and to these people, he showed little mercy. When a raiding party once breached their outer defences, he quickly closed all routes of escape. In close combat, he subdued them, capturing twenty malnourished men. After a brief consultation with Dorea, he marched them out, in plain view of their comrades hiding in the valley below. There, he executed them, leaving the bodies to the elements.

For over a year, Dorea and Rengal protected the scrolls of Psorsis from attack. Realising, then, that hiding behind their defensive works would not halt the bloodshed, they decided upon a bold plan. Picking thirty of his toughest men, Rengal trained them for attack. Working under the cover of darkness, he taught them all that he knew of hand-to-hand combat. With his engineers, he devised a cutting knife whose blade was lethal to those unfortunate enough to encounter it.

When not training, he consulted with Dorea. Together, they developed a plan which, they felt, would end the bloodshed once and for all. On a moonless night, with his men ready, he began his campaign. Dividing his men into two groups, they advanced quietly down the valley, approaching the old settlement from two flanks. The village lay quiet, its inhabitants asleep. No guard patrolled to give warning. At the signal, the low call of an owl echoing across the fields, the two groups advanced stealthily.

The traitors were caught in their beds. With the cries of battle ringing in their ears, they rose in a feeble attempt to defend themselves. Rengal, leading his men, attacked suddenly and ferociously. Single-handed, he despatched five traitors before making his way toward the central house, the former home of Midreas, the house of the leader of the rebels.

Four men brandishing stone knives blocked his path. He cut them down where they stood. He broke into the squalid hut. In the doorway, he met Pythmeas. He looked at the old man, shivering, terror on his face. Rengal felt no pity. Instantly, he plunged the knife into the traitor's throat and the elder fell, dead. Now, Rengal surveyed the darkened room. In the sleeping nook, at the far corner, he saw a pile of bedclothes, a pile that shook as he approached. Rengal bent, snatching away the cloth. On the floor before him lay Marthras, the weak son of a strong father. Rengal knew what must be done. With blood already on his hands, Rengal reached down and grabbed him by the hair, forcing him to stand. Marthras could not look at him. Rengal spat on the ground. "Surely you are not the offspring of Midreas," he said. With that, he thrust his knife deep into the heart of Marthras. He left him lying in the dirt, and strode to the door to help his fellow warriors.

With Marthras and Pythmeas dead, the discord ended. Leaderless, the rebels turned to Dorea and Rengal for guidance. Abandoning the former village altogether, it was decided to make the camp at the monument the people's permanent base. But the people were broken, demoralised by years of warring. Only two hundred of them survived, and of these, over fifty were enfeebled by starvation or age.

Dorea herself, now approaching her last years, saw that the Atlantean culture again faced extinction. She proposed a solution: a new generation that could gain back what they had lost in the recent years and that would have the wisdom, foresight, and ferocity necessary to survive. As old as she was, and though she had never married, Dorea took Rengal for her husband.

Despite her age, Doria became pregnant by Rengal. In the spring of the new year, she gave birth to a daughter, Kristiana. As she held the new-born infant, she prayed that here, at last, might be a new leader. A leader who combined the wisdom of

Midreas, the intelligence of Psorsis, the skill and daring of Rengal. She held the child up. Rengal bent to take her. And as he did so, Dorea breathed her last.

And so it was that the blood of Psorsis continued.

From the first, Kristiana proved to be a gifted child. By the time she was five, she was talking with the mathematicians, asking them to explain complex equations to her. By her thirteenth birthday, she had leaped beyond the bounds of existing thinking, and began delving into higher mathematics. No longer could her teachers help her. As her mind developed, she began looking for clues into the nature of the universe itself. Her teachers grew frightened at her knowledge and insight. They knew that no one, other than Psorsis himself, had understood what this young girl now sought to know.

Kristiana was gifted in other ways. She had the Atlantean talent for sensing sources of power. At night, alone, she would walk the perimeter of the half-completed monument. Below her, she sensed the forces that lay waiting. Forces which, she believed, only her grandfather understood. Putting out her hands, she felt the power buried beneath the earth. She stood, letting it wash through her; into her, permeating every crevice of her being. The great monument to Psorsis rose behind her. In it, she knew, lay the scrolls, buried in the earth. She knew that the scrolls held more than simple equations. They held the answers which she now sought. Answers which, she believed, would unravel the very secrets of the universe. Kristiana, though young, was not impatient. She would wait. One day, she knew that the scrolls of Psorsis would be opened. Until then, their power remained sealed.

Under the leadership of Rengal, the Atlantean survivors again prospered. Slowly, he built a new settlement directly under the shadow of the monument. For many years, work had ceased entirely on the mound, and now Rengal had no resources to direct towards it. Instead, he worked steadily to rebuild his civilisation.

The gatherers and farmers again brought in a plentiful

supply of food. His people no longer starved. The survivors were encouraged to multiply. He knew that to ensure cultural survival, he must increase the population. He talked with Kristiana. Though she was still young, now only sixteen, she chose to take a husband. Within a year, she was the mother to a child, a boy. They named him Psorsis, after his great-grandfather.

Kristiana balanced the fighting instincts of Rengal. She set up schools in the village, teaching mathematics to her fellow citizens. She persuaded the older engineers and scientists to pass on their knowledge to the younger people. Working closely with her people, Kristiana reawakened the yearning for knowledge that the Atlanteans had lost during the time of Marthras.

Rengal left Kristiana alone. As a fighter, he had no time for knowledge. Still, he recognised its importance and helped her where he could. They seldom clashed over policy. He took care of the basic needs of the community. She looked after the higher needs – and the future. And he knew that when he died, she would lead the people in his place.

It was twenty-five years after the defeat of Marthras. Rengal walked up the small path that led from the village to the monument. It was a bright summer's day. Insects droned over the grass and the birds sang brightly. Farmers toiled in their fields, and from his position at the top of the valley, Rengal looked down to see fishermen harvesting the river. He stood for a moment in thought.

"You've done much in your time, Rengal." The voice came from behind him. Startled, he turned. Kristiana stood amid the rocks of the monument. Her son, Psorsis, stood with her. Slowly, they walked down to join him.

"Yes," replied Rengal, turning back, "we have done many things together." He turned to her. "We have much to be proud of. The people have begot a thriving new generation. They no longer starve. With good fortune, I will see our village double in size before I die."

Kristiana smiled. "And so you shall, father."

He laughed. "Perhaps. I am no longer a young man, Kristiana. Sometimes, my bones tell me to rest awhile – longer, perhaps, than I would like to. My time is coming near. Soon, I think, you shall lead instead of me."

"Perhaps," she replied simply. Her gaze wandered. She turned back, facing the unfinished monument. He followed her gaze. He took a step forward, placing his hands on one of the great standing stones. He looked at her.

"You have never asked me about the monument," he said.

"What of it?"

He smiled. "Come, now, Kristiana. I'm old, but I'm no fool. The work on the monument is not complete and it should be. Your uncle, Midreas, knew that we must protect what lies beneath it. The scrolls of Psorsis. You know this too. Yet you have never pressed for its completion."

"It was not time. Other things were more important."

"And you let me complete my job. You let me lead in my own way." He looked at her uncomfortably. "And now?"

She returned his look. "What Midreas started should be completed," she stated.

He thought for a moment. "Yes." He studied her. "I am a fighter, Kristiana. Not an architect nor an engineer nor a mathematician. I can supply the strength, but I cannot resurrect the design that was once Midreas's."

She smiled. "I can do that."

"Yes," he said, walking over to her, "I believe you can. As we rebuild our society together, so shall we finish the monument." He touched her on the shoulder. Then, he turned, marching back down to the village with the energy of a man many years younger.

In the autumn, construction restarted on the monument to Psorsis. Once again, the great blocks of shale were hauled northwards from the valley. Slowly, they made their way up to the building site along a path of timbers. Men laboured and sweated, and ever standing by them was Kristiana.

Years earlier, she had studied the designs which Midreas

left behind, and she knew what he had intended. Now, using the power that was available to her, she subtly altered that design. Carefully, she checked and rechecked the location of the sunrise. On a chart, she plotted this, along with the location of the magnetic and water forces buried under the surface of the earth. Using her understanding of mathematics, she calculated the relationships between these tremendous sources of power. She recognised the potential which they offered, and the benefits which they would one day give to her people. The years passed, and slowly the monument took shape.

Rengal watched her and smiled. He was an old man now and shortly he would pass from the Place of the Sun to a new place inhabited by Psorsis, Midreas and his long-dead ancestors. The thoughts of dying did not bother him, however. He knew that the skills and foresight of Kristiana would lead the survivors of Atlantis to a new greatness. He saw that in her as she talked to her people. Even though he was still leader, she already led. He was wise enough to let her.

It was winter, the shortest day of the year. Rengal, now too weak to walk, lay in a litter, waiting. The past few days had seen a flurry of activity. The monument neared completion. In the very early hours of the morning, Kristiana entered his hut with two citizens. Rengal looked up at her. A fierce light of determination still lit the eyes of the old warrior.

"It is ready?" he asked, already knowing the answer.

"Yes," she replied. "Just as Midreas ordered."

He smiled briefly. Kristiana was dressed almost regally. A long gown of fine fur covered her. "Knowing you, Kristiana, I surmise that the monument is superior to the one Midreas ordered."

She returned his smile. "Perhaps."

"Come, then. It is time." The two men picked up the litter. Slowly, they walked up the small hill.

In the half-light, Rengal could see the great mound, and what he saw amazed him. It lay like a great, silent fortress. A wall of white quartz glistened even in the poor light. In its middle was an entrance and on each side, an army of standing stones stood, like sentinels guarding that entrance.

With effort, Rengal rose from his bed. Kristiana offered him her arm. "It is almost time. We must go in." A blazing torch was passed to her. Slowly, she led him through the entrance, down the stone-lined tunnel, and into the small interior chamber. He put his hands up to the great stones that lined the path. "I am pleased, Kristiana. It is a fitting place for the scrolls of Psorsis." He looked down at the ground beneath his feet. "I take it that the scrolls are still buried beneath us?"

"Yes," she replied. "For now."

He laughed shortly. "But for how long? Is it time to look at the great scrolls, Kristiana? Would you learn much?"

She did not reply immediately. At last she said, "Yes, I think it is time. I sense a new beginning for our people, Rengal." She touched the rock walls with her hand. "This place is much more than a refuge for the scrolls. It is a gate. A gateway into our future." Her eyes glowed with excitement, the fire from the torch reflecting off her long hair. "This place is a fortress of power. Of great forces. Midreas knew it when he selected the site. But I . . . " she looked at him and her look held great humility, " . . . I feel more."

Rengal studied her. "You have a gift. You sense our future, do you not, Kristiana? A new time of greatness. A new dawn for the people of Atlantis."

Excitement crept into her voice. "Yes. From here, from this place of rock and knowledge, our people shall grow. We shall move much farther than we ever have before. Out, beyond this place, we shall travel seeking still more knowledge. Until we will be able to look back at what we once were, at what we have become, and we shall know all. This great monument is the place of rebirth. And like a mother's womb, it shall protect us until we are ready to embark on our journey." She looked at her father. "Until that time, Rengal, we shall study. We shall look into the scrolls of Psorsis for answers. And those scrolls shall nourish us and protect us."

He smiled, a distance coming into his eyes. "I shall not live to see this. But you and your son – you shall guide our people towards a new dawn and new lands. Out of our poverty, we shall rise yet again!"

They heard, then, a shout from the outside. A shout of anticipation. Kristiana extinguished the torch, plunging them into darkness. "It is time. See!" she said, "see what Midreas bestowed on us!"

Together, they watched. Light began to filter into the darkened chamber and they could see the outlines of the rock tunnel, all the way up to the entrance of the monument. Through this tunnel, they saw the distant hills, outlined by the coming dawn.

Now, the great sun itself appeared, rising directly opposite the entrance; slowly, majestically. The light of the sun shone directly into the dim chamber; rays of light extended through the tunnel, up, up toward them, resting at last at their feet. At the exact centre of the monument. At the exact place where the scrolls of Psorsis lay buried.

"Dawn has come to our people," Rengal said. "Now, it is up to us to learn. On this day, the scrolls of Psorsis shall be opened."

12

"Outstanding!" Cathy whispered quietly, almost reverently. She stared up at the ceiling of the chamber, looking at the stars as they paraded overhead. "It's as if we were standing outside on a clear evening."

"Precisely!" Barnabus still stood on the milky-quartz dais. "In fact, you might as well be outside. What you are seeing is an exact reproduction of the heavens from this viewpoint. See?" He pointed toward the west. "That's Orion. And that small misty patch just below Orion's belt? That's M42, the nebula in Orion." He turned. "Over there, the Big Dipper. To its left, Cassiopeia. Straight up? The Northern Cross." He directed his look to his students. "It's all there. All of it. What you are seeing is a planetarium. A megalithic-age planetarium. But it has detail which even our modern facilities do not! And its power. Look!"

Slowly, Barnabus raised his right hand, pointing it toward the east. There the moon rose full, silent, majestic. "The moon is in its correct position. As we look, it appears as it appears today. We can see the Sea of Tranquillity from here, and the rays from Tycho. Now, we shall change it."

He flexed his hand and suddenly made a fist. Instantly, the moon sped towards them, hurtling up out of the black inkiness. Falling, falling towards them. Jonathan gasped involuntarily. "How . . . ?" he whispered. Then Barnabus relaxed his fist slightly. The moon slowed; then stopped. It seemed to be hanging only a few miles above them. It was so huge that it completely filled the ceiling of the chamber. Its light – the reflected light of a sun that was millions of miles distant – lit the room with its power.

"See?" said Barnabus. "See the detail?" He moved his arm slightly. Now, they seemed to glide upwards, as if suspended on a moving platform. Above them, the geography of earth's satellite unfolded. Mountain ranges thrust up into the vacuum. Craters from long-ago meteorite impacts littered the landscape. Vast plains of grey-white dust lay like ancient seas before them.

"Now, I will show you something." Barnabus moved his hand slightly. The moving landscape came to a stop. Slowly, the view changed, as if the platform upon which they stood rotated in mid-space. Suddenly, the horizon moved, a grey-white beach framed by the dark ocean of the universe. Then, to the west, a globe rose easily, purposefully, and that globe was Earth. "Behold," said Barnabus. "The cradle of mankind." They seemed to move closer to their home planet.

As they came closer, Barnabus flexed his hands again. For a moment Earth shimmered, like an indigo jewel thrown into a still pond. "It's beautiful," Jonathan whispered.

Barnabus's eyes twinkled. "So it is. But it offers a surprise. See if you can tell me what it is."

Above them, the earth rotated on its axis. All at once, they entered the night side. The pin-prick light of stars hovered beyond a black horizon. Now above them, the only light was of Earth's great oceans reflecting the light of the moon behind them.

Cathy spoke. "Where are the lights?"

Her teacher laughed with excitement. "Precisely. Where are the lights?"

"They have to be there."

"Do they?" Barnabus looked at them. "They would be there, Jonathan, unless there are no sources with which to make the light."

"But that's impossible! The land should be blazing with lights. Lights from cities. Towns."

"What if there were no cities or towns?" Their teacher

looked at them in amusement.

"I don't get it."

"What we're looking at, humble students, is Earth not of today, but of a couple of thousand years ago. Before the great cities. Before the advent of man-made kilowatt power. Before we had the knowledge to throw a thousand, million megawatts of light up into the dark unknown." Barnabus paused. "We're looking at a record. Of what this planet used to be. Now, watch." He rotated his hand slightly. Above them, the Earth began to spin. Cloud formations moved, great moon-reflected whorls against the black background. Faster and faster the planet moved, until it became an opaque blur. They watched, and as they did it began to slow again. Features became once more distinguishable and once again they looked at a hemisphere blanketed in darkness. This time, though, there was a difference.

"See? The lights of modern man." Among the continents, dots of light broke out like fireflies glowing in flight. Now they could make out geographic areas. North America faced them, and from their position they could see the glow of New York, Boston, Washington, DC, and the rest of the east coast.

Barnabus lowered his arm. "So, we have advanced to the present."

Jonathan and Cathy moved closer to the dais, never taking their eyes off the spectacle above them. "It's beautiful. I feel just like an astronaut. Hanging in orbit. Looking out at our planet."

Jonathan glanced at her. "You told me it's what you always wanted to do. Now you have your chance."

She returned his look. "It's not quite the same, Jonathan."

"No, I guess it isn't. You're still on Earth."

"But you don't have to be on Earth, Cathy." Standing on the dais, Barnabus towered above them, his head outlined in the faint glow of Earth light. "This . . . machine . . . is a door. A door into time. Into space. Into the past and the present. Into the unknown. The people who built this machine used it as a great tool. It enabled them to move outwards. Away from

Earth. It allowed them to explore the very edges of the universe."

Barnabus stretched out both arms. "Those who went before us left Earth to find out for themselves." He looked up. "In all likelihood, they are still out there. Somewhere. With this machine I can find them. With this I can go anywhere!" He thrust his arms out. Suddenly Earth swung beneath them, its horizon covered with lights disappearing into the floor of the chamber. Barnabus gestured with his outstretched arms, and now they hurtled through the universe. In front of them, Jupiter with its moons rushed into view. For a moment, they hovered, looking at the multi-coloured hues of the giant gaseous planet. Then, they sped on again. Outward, ever outward. Barnabus stopped briefly to look at Uranus with its rings tilted crazily, rotating at ninety degrees to the planetary ecliptic. Quickly, they dashed past the orbit of Pluto, and out beyond the solar system.

Now in deep space Barnabus raised his arms even higher. In front of them, the marvels of the universe began to unfold. Spiral galaxies danced into view like so many sparkling spinning tops. A great gaseous nebula, glowing from the light of concealed stars, hovered in the void. They stopped for a moment at a giant red sun, its huge nuclear furnace cooling, its own destruction foretold by the internal gravity which would one day cause its collapse. Barnabus plunged directly through this, and for a moment they were surrounded by the fires of hell, growing brighter and brighter, so bright that they blinded them. Then they were beyond, going onward, ever outward, and Barnabus, standing on the dais, kept his arms raised.

The room was dark again, the ceiling blank, except for the pulsing light from the great power source located deep beneath them. Barnabus, exhausted, sat on the floor by the dais. Jonathan and Cathy sat near him.

"To think that minds thousands of years ago developed this." Barnabus sat with his back propped up by the dais. "It puts our trinkets of technological development into perspective, doesn't it?"

Cathy nodded slowly. "It makes the space shuttle look like a toy. And the Hubble Telescope," she grimaced. "Mere wishful thinking."

"What I can't understand is how they knew." Jonathan still sat on the floor. "It is as if they visited all these places. How else could they possibly get pictures like that?"

Barnabus got up, the demon light from below playing on his squat body. He shook his head. "You don't understand, Jonathan. Those weren't pictures. What we saw was real. Except for that bit when we observed ancient Earth, the rest was actuality." Putting out his arms, he seemed to hold the room to him. "The forces in this room are somehow able to project us into any part of the universe which we wish to view. And into any time. With this machine, we could answer so many questions that scientists, philosophers and scholars have posed." Absently, he tucked his hands into his voluminous coat pockets. "For instance, what is the composition of a black hole? Or a quasar? Or what was the origin of the universe? What was the origin of the species of mankind? Who was Jesus Christ? Or Mohammed? Or Confucius? The list is endless."

He paused, his eyes twinkling behind rimless glasses. "In so many ways, of course, the machine is dangerous. With this, we could actually alter history. Can you imagine? For instance, what would have happened to world history if Adolf Hitler had won the Second World War? Or if John F Kennedy had not been assassinated? Or, closer to home, if King Billy had lost the Battle of the Boyne? Surely, Irish history would have taken a different course."

Jonathan got to his feet. "Come on, Barnabus." He looked around. "I mean, this is a great machine. Incredible. But really, it's just a great big movie theatre. It can show pictures, I know. But it couldn't possibly change history. How could it? Taking pictures of something doesn't alter history."

Barnabus smiled. "But you've seen only a fraction of the power of this place. This room is much, much more! A further illustration of that power is in order, I think!"

Barnabus looked through the maze of pockets in his overcoat. He pulled out an old pencil, bitten at the end. "How appropriate! An ancient method of communication used to prove the most sophisticated means which I've ever seen." He grasped the pencil firmly in his right hand. "Now, watch!" Barnabus climbed back up onto the dais. Immediately, the room again grew dark, the quartz of the dais glowed brighter, harnessing its endless energy. The ceiling of the chamber began to glow with countless stars.

Jonathan nudged Cathy. "I'd say that he's gone completely crackers," he whispered. "Does he think that he can use this room to transport things?"

Barnabus stood on the dais, arms outstretched. "Now. Where shall we send it to?"

"You're not serious, Barnabus."

He looked at them. "Deadly serious, my children. I repeat, where shall we send it to?"

Jonathan sighed, deciding to humour him. "I don't care. Why not the moon?"

"Any particular place there? Cathy, do you have any suggestions?"

She thought for a moment. "The Sea of Tranquillity. Why don't you put it down next to Apollo 11's lunar landing module? That way, it will have some company." She glanced at Jonathan, a slight scowl on her face.

Barnabus thought for a moment. "Right!" he said. "You could have chosen a more original place – but the Sea of Tranquillity it is!"

He flexed his hands and then clenched both fists, controlling. Slowly the moon rose over the horizon of the chamber. Again they watched as it hurtled toward them, its light filling the darkness of the room, until they seemed only a few miles from its surface. Barnabus stood on the dais, mumbling to himself. "Let's see, now. The Sea of Tranquillity. A little more north-east, I think. There we are!" Now, a vast plain of milky grey spread out before them. "The lunar landing module put down, I believe, on the coast of the sea somewhere. A little more to the left." Slowly, he moved his arms, and their view changed. "There! See that?" They looked. There, light glinted from a structure. Again, they headed towards the surface. A range of low hills became visible. Small craters pockmarked the area. In the centre of their field of vision, a small square was now apparent, increasing as they continued their descent. At last, they hovered close to it, perhaps twenty metres away. Barnabus looked around at them. "Is that it, Catherine?"

The girl stood transfixed. On the ceiling above her, the module rested. What they saw was only the first stage. Used initially as the descent rocket, it had acted as the launching pad for the astronauts' return flight. Now it sat, gold thermal material gleaming in the sun, the top of the lander burnt from the exhaust of the ascent module.

"I think that we should put our little message where it might be found, don't you?" Barnabus asked. He raised the pencil. Then, as Jonathan and Cathy watched, he did a strange thing. Reaching as high as he could, he seemed to rip open the image above him. A spectrum of light enveloped Barnabus: greens, reds, blues, golds, played across him. Sounds echoed through the chamber, like sand blown by the wind. And then, for a moment, Barnabus appeared transparent. Through his body, they could see the module, the surface of the moon, the footprints which had remained unchanged for more than twenty years. His arm now was a part of what they saw, and reaching even higher, he carefully placed the pencil on the surface of the module.

"There," he said. "Now any who come this way will know that we have been here, too."

13

The work on the scrolls took many years. At first, Kristiana could not fathom the intricate mathematical formulae at all. Psorsis had gone much further than any mathematician of his era. Kristiana knew that. She also knew that if she compared her intellect to Psorsis's, she was a mere child. Still, she struggled to learn.

The mathematical equations were laid out neatly, protected between resinous membranes which, she knew, were a form of glass, the secret of its manufacture now lost to the Atlanteans. For hours she pored over them, only stopping when her son, Psorsis, the great-grandson of the mathematician, brought her home to rest. She became a recluse, a stranger to the rest of the community, and as the days of study turned to months, and then to years, her fellow-citizens shied away from her. More than one muttered that she had turned into a witch, retreating, as she did, every day into the confines of the monument to study by torchlight.

Kristiana's husband, one of Rengal's bravest warriors, had died in a freak accident some time back. While she studied, her son – young though he was – took charge. Because of the work of Rengal and his mother, the community had thrived. Good harvests were brought in by the farmers. There was food in abundance. Still, now and again the old passions mounted, and Psorsis would step in to solve a dispute or negotiate peace between fighting neighbours. Often, the youth could be seen standing between two adults twice his age, listening to both sides of an argument. At last, he would pass judgement. The people – his people, now – saw the wisdom in those judgements and followed his advice.

On the few occasions when his advice was ignored, Psorsis saw to it that order was maintained. He recruited warriors from his village, and he was not above using them to make a point for the sake of peace. Still, on the few times that he used physical force, his people saw the wisdom even in that and supported him.

Under the guidance of their new leader, the village expanded. The rough huts that had been built around the protective shadow of the monument were knocked down and rebuilt. With their food supply restored and peace the norm, the people once again started to have children. The cry of newborn infants was heard. With his warriors, Psorsis also explored the countryside, seeking out new areas for potential settlement and food gathering.

Psorsis saw his task as simple: to maintain the good fortune of the village, and to allow his mother time for study. In the mornings, he accompanied her to the monument. At midday, he took her food. In the late evening, he walked her back to their hut. During all this time he protected her. Sometimes, he would go into the monument with her. On those occasions, he would look inquisitively at the scrolls, asking questions about their mathematical complexities, leaping lightly from one intellectual platform to another. In him, Kristiana saw a blending of their past leaders: the intellectual curiosity of Psorsis; the wisdom of Midreas; the leadership and bravery of Rengal. She knew that the people of Atlantis had a great leader now and she took comfort in this. Her work was with the scrolls; they held the key to a power greater than any her people had ever known. Still, the formulae of her grandfather were frustrating. Many nights, she would walk down the path towards home, Psorsis guiding her, unable to see with tiredness.

One night, Psorsis arrived later than usual. He found his mother hunched over the rocky outcrop that she used as a desk, the light from a smoking torch playing unevenly upon her face. Before her, a page from the scrolls lay open, half-covered by her long black hair. He called to her softly, not wishing to disturb her.

"Mother? It's very late."

She sighed. "So it is." She rose suddenly, fiercely, her face masked in frustration. "The answer is here! I'm certain of it!"

He smiled. "Where? Let me see." In the dim light of the torch, she pointed to a series of complex equations.

"Do you see? Here. This is the kernel of your great-grandfather's work. This seems to indicate a relationship among the universal laws of nature. It somehow shows how the power in nature is interconnected."

He studied the equations intently, looking for the combinations and theoretical nuances which she saw. He looked up at her. "Which forces are related?" he asked bluntly.

She shook her head sharply. "I don't know. Some of them? All of them? I'm not sure." She paced in the small confines of the rock-enclosed room. The light from the torch flickered in the air. She talked to him as she walked. "It's only conjecture. But your great-grandfather seems to posit that all things in nature have an inherent power. The air we breathe. The rocks of the earth. The flesh of our bodies. The waters flowing in the ground beneath us. Everything in nature has a power which goes beyond its physical limitations."

He thought for a moment. "And these equations . . . ?"

She stopped. "Indicate that we can tap into these forces. This power."

"For what purpose?"

"That, of course, is the ultimate question. Psorsis believed, apparently, that the power could be used to accomplish many tasks." Quickly, she sorted through a pile of protected manuscripts. "See here?" She pointed to notes on a page. "Here, Psorsis hypothesises that this power, if tapped and channelled correctly, can be used as an instrument of transport. It can be used to move matter from one location to another, instantly."

"What kind of matter?" her son asked absently.

"Any kind of matter, apparently. Rocks. Trees. Animals."

"Animals. Including man?"

She looked fully into his face. "Apparently so."

"You said 'transport'. Transport to where?"

She was silent for a moment. "Anywhere."

"Anywhere?" She nodded. He looked at her uncertainly, then down at the scrolls. "You mean anywhere in our domain? Perhaps as far as the great sea to the east of here?"

"No. I mean *anywhere*. Used correctly, the power can take us to the next valley. Across the sea. Back to our destroyed continent . . . or off the face of this planet." She paused. "Anywhere, Psorsis. Anywhere in the universe."

He pondered on what she said, excitement at last rising in his voice. "You said that the power can be used to accomplish many tasks. This is just one of them?"

She nodded. Quickly, she began paging through the scrolls. "See here? This indicates that natural power can be used as a weapon. A weapon of unimaginable force. Capable, perhaps, of destroying mountains, if not continents." She pointed again. "Here? This states that time itself can be surmounted. By controlling the power, modulating its frequency and power output, we can move through time much as we walk across a field. And here?" She pointed yet again. "This hypothesises an ability to transpose our thoughts. Through this, we would be capable of moving our minds into any natural element which we choose. Of becoming, if you will, that which we are thinking. So. If I wish to become this rock," she rested her hand on her stone desk, "I become the rock. If I desire to become a tree, I become a tree. If my objective is to be the sun itself, I become the sun."

He nodded, comprehending. "And by becoming, we understand."

"Yes," she said simply. "We understand. We would come to a knowledge of everything that the universe holds. We would exist, no longer restricted by our physical bodies, but in the never-ending sequence of events that composes nature. In the core of nature, itself."

They sat for a moment in silence. "So. This is the legacy of my great-grandfather."

"Yes. Through this, he has given us much more than merely the key to survival. Much more than our Atlantean greatness. He has given us the very key to immortality."

Psorsis looked at his mother, the torchlight reflecting in his eyes. "The question, therefore, is our ability to tap into the natural power necessary to achieve that greatness."

"Yes."

He peered once again at the scrolls, and at the series of complex equations that held the key to infinite power. "I shall think about it, Mother. Tomorrow, we shall study again." Then he led her out of the monument, and to their beds. But as they walked through the still night, his mind considered the many possibilities, and he pondered on these.

The answer to the mystery was quite easy, as it turned out. Psorsis thought of it suddenly, while stalking a deer. In his right hand, the spear rested easily. The deer, downwind of him, moved cautiously, grazing on the sweet grasses still wet with morning dew. Psorsis crept closer, silently, inching within throwing distance. He was there, at last, and gathering his skills and energies, he launched the spear. Forcefully, driving it home into the clean flanks. The animal sank slowly to its knees and then toppled.

He walked quickly to it through rough heather, knife ready to dispatch his prey. It was unnecessary. The deer was dead. The spear had driven cleanly through its side, piercing its heart. Quickly, he pulled the shaft from the warm body. The dark red blood was already congealing in the short, dense coat of soft-brown hair. "I'm sorry, deer," he thought. "But your meat is needed for our nourishment, your hide for our warmth. Your life-force shall not be wasted but will live in our people for as long as we exist."

He saw it then. Looking at the deer, he was suddenly one with it, as he was one with his people. He rose slowly, his hand wet with blood. He put it to his mouth, licking the liquid, feeling it in his mouth, in his throat, the rich smell penetrating his nostrils. For a moment, he was no longer himself. He was the deer. But he was more than that. He was that oak tree growing tall and proud, leaves rippling in the spring breeze. He was the rock, solid, sure, impenetrable. He was the bird, singing, moving swiftly in pursuit of wind-tossed insects. His mind focused, and for a moment the mathematical symbols of his great-grandfather spun and danced, moving now apart, now together, and finally into a definitive pattern. His mind flexed and the pattern changed, symbols moving into random possibilities, like the forces which gathered, invisible – yet real – around him. Yet he knew that they were not random. Like nature, they were related to each other; constants and variables, waiting only for the shift in thinking that would provide their focus. A bird called. The pattern moved once again. He saw it clearly, shimmering like a leaf blowing in a soft breeze. He dropped the spear, and ran back to the village to find his mother.

It took them many days to rearrange the equations into a working mathematical model and the application of that model took many months. First, they delved back into the architecture of the monument. Working together, they found the forces that Midreas had laid at their disposal, knowing even then that they would one day be of value. In the Atlantean way, they divined the powers that lay below them. Magnetic variations, powerful yet elusive, rolled in and out of the confines of the monument. Buried beneath them, they sensed the great rivers of tumbling, swirling waters, moving down dark tunnels and canyons, vast untapped sources of power waiting to be used. And far below those, the great molten energy of the earth itself churned, confined for now but waiting to be tapped.

They studied once again the positioning of the monument. The sun, rising above the far valley walls, warmed the quartz face of the entrance. Quartz, responding to the light, generated heat. Here, too, was power. Now, it was up to them to focus these vast resources on a single objective.

Work again began at the monument, but this time, with a

different purpose. Unquestioning, hundreds of workers began the excavation. The scrolls were carefully wrapped, and stored again in the vessel now four generations old. Carefully, a great chamber was dug out beneath the existing floor of the monument. The size, shape and position of the chamber were determined by the confluence of power below and above.

When the excavation was completed, its interior was lined with quartz chippings. These glowed in the light of workers' torches, as if already accumulating the power which they would soon harness.

At last, the chamber was ready. From the far south, a great block of quartz was brought, using the route devised by Midreas. It was hauled at last to the village, and a team of masons worked it into a rough dais. In this, Kristiana asked that an interior hollow be carved. This was then covered with a single sheet of quartz so finely engineered that, when laid, the joining seams were invisible.

By means of levers, the finished quartz dais was lowered slowly into the chamber and mounted on a deep layer of quartz chippings. It was aligned in such a manner as to attract the forces that moved restlessly beneath it. When all was ready, Kristiana and her son brought the scrolls of Psorsis into the finished chamber. She approached the quartz dais. She ran her hand gently around its perimeter, the dais rotated slowly, the quartz glowing with an interior energy. It opened, revealing an interior vault. Into this space she carefully placed the scrolls. "Now," she said simply, "it is finished."

The scrolls themselves were the final piece of the puzzle. The glass protecting them acted as an energy conduit. Through them, the energy surrounding them, contained in nature's elements, would be focused and fused into a source of unlimited power. With only her son Psorsis watching her, Kristiana took a deep breath and mounted the dais. She cleared her mind of all things. Then, concentrating on her own power within, she raised her arms. The quartz glowed. Radiant energy suffused the milky whiteness. Slowly, the floor of the chamber, dark grey stone, became translucent. Psorsis looked down. For a moment, he was startled, drawing back. But then he understood. Below him, the forces of nature appeared. The great flowing rivers, the forces which he had long felt but never seen, crashed and tumbled, falling and swirling through the great internal chasms. And below this, he saw the light of power, the red, primordial energy of the earth itself move relentlessly, the great force controlled by the huge pressures which contained it. Psorsis looked up. His mother, concentrating in order to apply what they had learned, flexed her wrist. Quickly, the room darkened. Kristiana looked up, up at the ceiling of the quartz-encrusted chamber. He followed her gaze, not understanding at first, but then knowing that the fruits of Psorsis's study at last lay before him.

The ceiling glowed with the countless stars of the universe. And in the east the moon rose.

Kristiana quickly explored the extent of their new-found power. With her son at her side, she discovered that the earth was only a small island in a system of nine planets; that these nine planets revolved around a munificent sun at the edge of a whirlpool of millions of stars. The spiral lay like an emerald island in a vast ocean of nothingness. But beyond floated hundreds and hundreds of other spirals, each composed of countless stars, many stars having their own planets, their own life forms. She wondered at the spirals. To her, they seemed like the whirling waters that rushed so powerfully just below the surface of the monument. She wondered what power these great gatherings of suns offered, and marvelled at the possibilities.

One day, sitting outside the monument, she talked to Psorsis about these. "These whorls of suns are much like the whorls of the great rivers which flow below us, my son. I think that the power offered by this multitude of stars must be vast. If we could harness their power, just think of what our abilities might be. We should use this potential." Kristiana thought for a moment. With her finger, she drew a figure in the dust. Psorsis saw what she drew.

She looked up at Psorsis. "What does that remind you of?"

He thought for a moment. "The swirling waters of our earth."

"Yes," she nodded. "And they also remind me of the whirling stars of the firmament which we have seen in the ceiling of the chamber."

He agreed, and Kristiana said, "This symbol represents the powers inherent in the earth. And the powers that we believe to be in the stars. I would like us to remember that, Psorsis." She sat near the entrance to the monument. Her eyes came to rest on the great stone which guarded it. "Don't you think that we might carve this symbol there?" She pointed. "At the very entrance to the monument – ? In this way, it marks the entrance to two types of power, the powers of earth and the powers of the universe."

Psorsis agreed. He rose to his feet. "I will have it done immediately." Then he stood thinking to himself. "Is there not another symbol we might use, Mother?"

She smiled. "And that is?"

Beside her figure, he drew in the dirt. His figure was much more simple than his mother's.

"What does it mean?" she asked.

It was his turn to smile. "At the bottom of the triangle rest two foundations of our new civilisation. To one side is my great-grandfather, Psorsis, who has given us the keys to power. To the other, Midreas, who protected those keys."

He pointed to the figure's apex. "At the top is you, Mother, who have unlocked the door to our future."

She looked, and agreed. "It is good, what you say. You will have this seen to?"

"Immediately."

The symbols of Kristiana soon covered the great stone. When they were finished, she touched the stone, her fingers tracing the living symbols. Psorsis stood by her. "It is good, is it not?"

"Now, future generations will know what we have done here. And what power lies here."

In the months that followed, mother and son explored many places within the universe. With the powers and knowledge which their long-dead ancestor Psorsis had revealed to them, they saw wonders. Stars were born and died in front of them. They explored many planets, some barren, others alive with entities foreign to their eyes. Often, they found worlds much like Earth itself, only with certain differences. Once, they plunged through a star system, visiting a world of oceans, green plants, and blue skies. In the seas, they found great creatures, much like whales, only many times larger than anything their people had previously seen. Huge bulbous mouths screened the waters, collecting the tiny animals which swam there. Torpedo-like hunters, shaped much like sharks, swam in the depths, feeding on pink and green amoeba-like creatures which floated in the currents. On land, great six-legged mammals grazed on vegetation. And winged creatures flew through a humid, warm atmosphere, heavy with the smells of living things.

The difference in this world was the sky. Hanging above this basket of life, three suns moved in a circuitous path dictated by their interdependent gravities. Two of the suns, still relatively young, lit the little world with sunlight much like earth's own sol. But a red giant, hanging as a huge, ruddy disk, made the world a place of reds and purples. It was a strange planet, but one with many possibilities. Carefully, Kristiana noted its location.

Kristiana also learned to use the power of the monument to move through time. At first, she ventured uneasily. Standing on the milky-white quartz dais, arms outstretched, she moved slowly back in time. She watched herself and Psorsis awakening the previous day. Going for their early breakfast. She went back a few months, looking on as workers carved the great whorl-symbols which now adorned many of the stones surrounding the monument to the scrolls of Psorsis.

As she gained confidence, Kristiana moved back further in time. She watched as the great stones of the monument were brought up the valley, with Rengal in the lead. Then Midreas stood before her, alive, his intelligent face glowing with excitement as he chose the location for the monument. She saw him, too, as he walked up over the little hill, followed by a group of starving, ill-clad survivors, and looked for the first time upon the Place of the Sun.

Finally, she gathered her courage and went back even further. Now, the ceiling of the chamber was alive with the civilisation which was Atlantis. Great cities thrust up from a continent alive with an active people. Huge fleets fished the surrounding seas for food. Great factories manufactured clothing, foods, and other goods which the Atlanteans required. She saw this, disbelieving. Compared with what they had been, the survivors of Atlantis had accomplished little. She mused on this, her mind alive at what the future might yet hold for them.

Suddenly, she was in a great place of learning. Before her sat an older man, a book of equations before him. He smiled as he wrote, and she knew that here was Psorsis himself, writing the scrolls which now permitted her to see him. It had taken many years to put to use the knowledge which he bequeathed them, but she knew that he would be proud.

And then, a strange thing happened. Psorsis stopped writing. He put down the writing implement, and looked at Kristiana, as if he could see her. Then he spoke, as if to her alone.

"Time is a strange creature," he said. "One day we are here. The next day gone. Folded into nothingness by a linear course of events. The question becomes, then: what happens when we attempt to alter the straight path of time?" He laughed slightly, as if enjoying a secret. "Future generations will find out, of course. They will learn to bend time – and space, too, for that matter – to suit their own purposes. With enough knowledge, and enough power, the future can go anywhere. Towards anything. Or away from anything."

He paused in thought. "Some day, people will wonder at the destruction of our civilisation. No one believes me yet, but our great civilisation will perish in a ball of fire and terror never yet known by man. And when they do at last believe me, they will react slowly." He shook his head sadly. "For many, it will be too late. But perhaps the future of our people can be safeguarded."

Psorsis looked up, his long white hair moving as if in a breeze. "Yet even when they do know their tragic destiny, they will still not recognise it for what it is. Our destruction was no accident." He turned again to where Kristiana stood, as if sensing her presence. "Those who are to come must recognise this and take heed. Something, someone caused our destruction. And what has happened once can happen again." He looked gravely towards her. "Look!" he said. "See what is happening to us. Find out why. If you know these things, you may find the truth. And in that, you may be able to protect yourself and the future destiny of the people of Atlantis."

At once, the vision faded. In its place, Kristiana looked out on a cluster of planets circling a sun in their steady orbits. She looked, and recognised them. She saw Earth, the blue of its oceans washed by the sun-reflecting white clouds. She saw nothing unusual at first, but she watched.

Now, she saw a vague, ghostly shape hurtling through

space. As it approached the sun, heat struck its core, and from this a great billowing gas cloud sprang, a ghostly-white shadow following in its path. Kristiana realised that she was looking at a comet and she knew that she saw the comet that had destroyed her people.

She shook her head, puzzled. "How?" she whispered to herself. "How could this possibly have struck the Earth?" The comet moved harmlessly, millions of miles from any planet. Surely, it was not possible for this to strike Earth, she thought.

But as she watched, a strange thing happened.

As she looked, space itself seemed to ripple, as if a boy had thrown a pebble into a calm lake. For a moment, the sun and planets dissolved, and she felt a power – greater than any she had known – surge through the vision. It was as if she was standing beside a living bolt of lightning. The force of it charged the air within the chamber. She felt her hair move, blown as if by the early gusts of a great storm. She stood firm on the dais, watching. Slowly, the vision cleared.

Now she saw the comet change course. As she watched, it moved across the orbits of the other planets, like an intelligent being. It pointed now directly at Earth, and as she watched, it plunged through the outer atmosphere, striking at the heart of the planet. The explosion which followed was terrible to look at. Fire, earth and smoke fumed into the sky, forming a great pall. She knew that in the intense smoke and heat, the burned fragments of her ancestors moved restlessly.

Her son found her an hour later. She sat by the dais, crying. It took him many hours to learn that she had witnessed the destruction of their people. And it was some time later that she told him that the destruction had been intentional.

14

"You can't just walk out through that. You don't know what you'll be stepping into."

Barnabus was walking quickly through the door to the chamber, a mountain of personal belongings in his arms. He threw the stuff on to the floor, once again alive with motion.

"I don't mean to be obstinate, Jonathan, but yes, I do intend going and that's that. Now the least you can do is to stop standing around and lend a hand."

"But why?"

He looked at his students, and shook his head. "Have you no curiosity? No interest in knowledge? If Edison had thought as you, we'd still be trying to read by oil-lamp. Orville and Wilbur Wright would have stuck to their bicycle shop rather than move men toward flight. Neil Armstrong's steps would have been along a pavement rather than on the surface of the moon. Men have always sought to understand. It is how we grow. Here," he indicated the chamber, "this unique apparatus, made by men God only knows how many thousands of years ago, offers me a challenge. I intend to accept it."

Catherine sat on the dais, her arms crossed. "Barnabus, how can you possibly go when you don't know where you're going?"

"Oh, but I do!" He approached her quickly, his coat flapping around him as he walked. "I intend to look for the people who built this."

Catherine, seated on the dais, gazed at him obstinately.

"And where, pray tell, might they be? Don't tell me. Alpha Centauri?"

"Our closest stellar neighbour, yes. A good thought. But no, you're wrong. They're much further away than that."

Jonathan threw his hands into the air. "You don't even know if they've left Earth."

"Don't I, Jonathan? Excuse me, Catherine. You'll have to unseat yourself. Now, the pair of you, watch."

He put both hands flat on the dais. Instantly, the room darkened slightly, the glow of the underground fire banked once again as the room tapped into its great power. Overhead, the stars appeared once more. Only this time, a grid was superimposed over the stars. "Look familiar?"

"It's a map."

"Precisely. The last time, we travelled where we wanted without the use of coordinates. Now, however, we see the stars properly laid out with grid coordinates. Through this, the ancients were able to communicate a specific grid reference to a fellow traveller."

"It still doesn't tell us where your ancients have gone to, Barnabus."

"Doesn't it?" He motioned to the girl. "Catherine, come over here. Look at the surface of the dais." Slowly, she walked to the glowing quartz. "Do you see anything of particular interest?"

She looked carefully. The translucent material seemed to have no depth or definition. Certainly, she could not see any writing. Then she noticed the series of indentations glowing slightly from the power of the dais. She looked up at Barnabus. "You mean these?"

"Well observed! And what do you suppose they are?"

She looked again, carefully. Suddenly, she knew. "It's the whorl. The carved whorl of Newgrange."

"Again correct. The symbol of this structure. Put your hand on it."

She did so. The symbol glowed and pulsated. "Now," said Barnabus, "look up!"

They looked. For a moment, they could not see anything. "Try the constellation of Pegasus." Quickly, Cathy found the Big Dipper, then Cassiopeia and finally, the quadrangle that marked Pegasus. On the ceiling of the chamber, within the constellation of Pegasus, the whorled symbol of Newgrange hung, pulsing slowly, rhythmically.

"That's where they are. They have gone there. Is it any wonder that modern archaeologists have long speculated on what happened to the builders of Newgrange? For years, scientists wondered what became of them. No trace of these early builders could be found. And is it any wonder?" Barnabus put his hands deeply into his pockets, contemplating. "They couldn't be found because they were no longer here! For whatever reason, they gave up their old way of life on this planet, and sought a new existence – a new life among the stars!"

"You're speculating, Barnabus," said Cathy.

"Come on, Barnabus. You're talking crazy," said Jonathan.

He shrugged. "Perhaps. But there's only one way of finding out." He took his hands off the dais. The map of stars and the symbol quickly faded. "Now, do give me a hand with my equipment, if you please."

Jonathan and Catherine looked at each other, and then at their teacher. Jonathan turned, then, his face set. "I can't speak for Cathy," he said. "But you're not going if I'm not going."

His teacher stood, stunned. "What? Of all the impertinence coming from you, a mere student." His face set. "Who's going to stop me?"

Cathy chimed in. "We are."

"That's right," Jonathan agreed. He paced around the room, his face as determined as his teacher's. "Of course, we can't actually stop you from going. But I would imagine that certain national and international authorities would be most interested in this room. Don't you think so, Cathy?"

"I certainly agree." She looked directly at her teacher. "I'm certain that NASA would be very interested in it, for one. And I can think of a dozen other agencies who would love to do some in-depth research on this place."

Barnabus leaned heavily against the dais. "But that's blackmail!"

"Call it what you will." Catherine moved to stand by Jonathan. "We're not letting you go out there on your own. It's too risky."

"Come on, Barnabus. You might even find that we can help."

Barnabus considered for a moment. "Well, considering the options, I imagine that bringing you along is the best."

"Right! So when do we leave?"

Barnabus looked at them. "Well, actually, I was planning to leave right now. If you would ever give me a hand with these things, we could do so immediately."

The pair jumped to lend a hand. Quickly, they piled the few items on top of the dais. Barnabus mounted the quartz block, and turned to them. "Stand very close to the dais. When I say so, I want you to move quickly. Climb up beside me on the quartz, and do exactly as I do."

He turned from them and, reaching down, touched the carving of the whorl of Newgrange firmly. Instantly, the symbol pulsed and started to gyrate, glowing on the ceiling of the great chamber. Barnabus once again extended his arms. The glow from the energies beneath intensified as the power was focused into a brilliant, controlled force. The quartz dais pulsed with energy and the constellations grew bright above them.

Now Barnabus guided them toward the constellation of Pegasus. Stars moved like shadows beside them, at first small dots of light, and then receding quickly down the walls of the chamber. A white dwarf star appeared suddenly, momentarily blinding the chamber in a wall of intense light. Just as suddenly, it was gone, quickly moving behind them.

In front of them the whorl of Newgrange still showed, guiding them towards a distant objective. For a while, it remained faint, distant. But now it grew, larger and larger, filling the room, the chamber alive with its golden radiance. At last, they reached it, passing through it as if through a golden cloud shimmering with the rays of sunset.

Barnabus flexed his wrist. They lost their forward motion, now hanging, suspended in a dark velvet tapestry, the universe stretching out in all directions. Below them, a fantastic, almost surreal sight greeted them. A trinity of suns spun silently. Two of these with the apparent brightness of Earth's sun circled around a great Red Giant, trapped in orbit by the larger star's gravitational pull. The giant, cool enough to allow them to look directly into it, was mottled with dark sun-spots, speeding across its great face. The two captured suns, kept like playful dogs on short leashes, hovered in the glow of their great red master. The gravitational fields created by the three suns must have been enormous. As they watched, a solar flare of fantastic proportions arced majestically away from one of the children stars. Captured immediately by the gravity of the Red Giant, they watched as the hot gasses began to spin, sinking quickly toward the giant, becoming absorbed in the glowing redness.

Around this warring family, a handful of planets spun, strung like pearls on a jeweller's table.

Barnabus was the first to react. "It must be incredibly unstable. Look at the way the giant is bleeding the other suns of material. And in all likelihood, it's been doing so for millions of years. Sooner or later, the masses of the suns will change significantly. When that happens, only God Himself knows what will happen."

Slowly, Barnabus brought them closer to the system. They passed through the orbits of the two outer planets without stopping. Four inner planets, reflecting the light of their three parent suns, waited for them.

"Which one, Barnabus?"

"I don't know. I suggest we take a look. Let's try the nearest one." Slowly, he rotated their view, and crept up to the planet, hanging only miles above its surface.

"It's smooth!"

He looked back at Catherine. "So it is," he stated simply.

What greeted them seemed impossible. The surface of the planet was a brilliant white. An opal hanging in the void of space, it had no features, no atmosphere. Its uniformly smooth surface seemed as slick and as empty as a sheet of ice. The planet was dead, a great hunk of white rock spinning slowly through time.

"That's not natural, is it?" asked Catherine.

Barnabus thought for a moment. "I wouldn't say so, no. But many things occur in nature which go well beyond our comprehension. The people of Newgrange cannot possibly have migrated here, anyway. Let's move on."

Their next stop was also fruitless. The landscape was pockmarked by huge craters which dotted most of the surface of the planet. Through them, great fissures ran like rivers, boiling magma pumping from the core of the planet. But here there was an atmosphere. Smoke curled restlessly upward, blanketing the planet in a thick brown haze. Orbiting around the planet, boulders miles across spun crazily. As they watched, a trail of brilliant white light flashed through the murky atmosphere. On the surface of the planet, they saw the impact, smoke and tonnes of earth blown skyward, adding to the brown haze.

"Obviously, what we're seeing is the demise of a planet. The rocky chunks in orbit were, I believe, once parts of a moon. Somehow, it has been blown apart." Barnabus wiped his glasses as he speculated. "Now and then, the gravitational force of the planet pulls the lunar material out of orbit. Unfortunately, the atmosphere is not heavy enough to entirely disintegrate this material prior to impact. The result, I'm afraid, is devastation." He turned to them heavily. "I suggest that we move on."

Their third choice seemed more promising. The planet that moved upward to greet them appeared to be much like Earth. Great blue oceans contrasted vividly with voluminous white cloud formations. Brown and green continents lay majestically below them. "Certainly they came here," Barnabus whispered. "As humans, they required breathable air. A climate in which they could grow crops. This planet would seem to offer such possibilities." He glanced back at the pair, standing close to the dais. "Come. We'll go closer."

They ventured nearer, hovering at first just above the atmosphere as Barnabus surveyed the area. Encouraged, he moved them down again, down through towering fronts of cloud, down toward a sea surging against a stiff breeze. Quickly, they glided across, huge waves rising up to greet them. In the distance, they could see land. Jonathan saw it first. "There! On the horizon."

Barnabus answered. "I see it."

A city moved toward them. Immense buildings towered into the sky, needles of glinting light which disappeared into the low-lying cloud deck. But what was most surprising was the material out of which they were constructed. It glittered and flashed in the sunlight. Surely, thought Barnabus, they cannot be made of gold? He halted for a moment, and they hovered, studying the golden city from a distance.

"Jonathan, Catherine. Now, please come up on to the dais. I believe, lady and gentleman, that we have arrived."

Quickly, they mounted the dais. Barnabus moved again. They passed over a harbour with huge ships tied up to great piers. Buildings towered above them. Silent. Welcoming. All seemed peaceful. Quiet. They moved closer, and now Barnabus raised his hands. Once again, he seemed to reach up into the picture that was above them. A roaring met them, a smell like oxidised metal permeated the chamber. Barnabus seemed to take hold of the illusion above them. He pulled. The vision came closer to them, now hovering just above their heads. "Now," he said, "take hold of what you see, and reach!" Jonathan and Cathy did so. The quartz dais grew brighter, the power of the monument now focused on its single objective. Slowly, the vista of the city sank towards them, joining with the chamber, covering and absorbing the three travellers. For a single moment, they were part of both worlds, bodies transparent as their physical elements were controlled by the forces surrounding them. They were in the void, the great vortex of power, light flashing around them, blinding, too great to understand. It flooded their senses, and they stood, almost paralysed, flotsam awash on a great wave of energy.

Now, too late, Jonathan saw what was before him and shouted, terrified. He tried to withdraw his arms, calling to the others to escape, but they were caught, now part of the vision confronting them. Then, Cathy and Barnabus saw it, but they too were helpless.

Above them, the clouds had parted. The buildings, golden ribbons towering hundreds of meters above them, ended suddenly. Truncated. The tops, twisted metal, glowed still from the damage that had been inflicted. As they watched, a searing white finger of light reached out from a towering cloud. It touched one of the ribbons of gold. Instantly, the top of the structure sheered, falling almost majestically into the city which lay below. Great globules of liquid gold followed its descent.

The three stood now on a field of flat white rock watching as the finger stabbed, again and again, at the golden web of a defenceless city.

15

That the destruction of the civilisation of Atlantis had happened at all was intolerable. The fact that it was premeditated shocked Kristiana and Psorsis. To their knowledge, the Atlanteans had never considered the possibility of life beyond Earth before. Their forebears had assumed, wrongly, that only Earth nurtured intelligent creatures. Certainly, the forces that directed the comet which brought destruction to their people must have been intelligent. The mathematical precision of what Kristiana now believed to be a well-planned and well-executed attack indicated a level of intellectual development far superior even to that which the Atlanteans had possessed in their zenith.

More significantly, the concentrated energy required to control the comet, to change its direction, and then to direct it precisely towards a specific target must be vast indeed. Kristiana and Psorsis considered this carefully. They recognised that the beings behind the attack must be intellectually superior to them. It followed that whoever or whatever designed the attack must still exist. And if so, they had powers not only to observe Earth in detail but to follow with another attack if they so desired.

For the first time, Kristiana knew fear. She did not like knowing that at any moment the survivors of Atlantis might be obliterated from the face of the earth, that all their work, their toil, could be convulsed into a seething pit of torn, blood-soaked earth.

Quickly she gathered the elders of her tribe in conference.

They met in the chamber of the monument. Since the chamber had become empowered with the forces of the earth, its physical properties had changed. The floor glowed blood-red from the forces buried far below. The great swirling underground rivers were visible, churning through the rock on their journey to the open sea. And around them, the rock walls, their atomic structure energised by the dynamo beneath, lit the chamber with strange light.

A dozen men entered the chamber, Kristiana and Psorsis in the lead. These elders, men trusted for their judgement, bravery and expertise, had not been allowed in the chamber since its empowerment. Kristiana heard mutterings of "witchcraft" and "black magic". She turned to them, waiting for their full attention, her gown of white wool glowing blood red from the hell-fire burning beneath her.

She raised her hands for silence. "My people. For over a hundred years we have protected the scrolls of Psorsis, not knowing what heritage my grandfather offered to us. As you all know, I have spent many years studying these. With my son, I have tried to fathom the mathematics contained in them. Much of the knowledge contained in the scrolls we still do not understand. But we have unlocked some of their secrets and we have applied many things which Psorsis sought to teach us."

She pointed to her feet. "What you see below is the great energy of the Earth, harnessed by us, empowering us to do many, many strange yet wonderful things. It is not witchcraft, Leandor." She turned to an old man, one of her elders, with long white hair hanging to his shoulders. "It is not black magic. What you see is the application of great knowledge, and an understanding of the powers of nature."

Her son, a leader now in his own right, also spoke. "The power of our planet is not infinite but, harnessed correctly, it provides us with amazing capabilities." He looked carefully at them, noting the fear on their faces. "With this power, and through the mechanisms in this chamber, we can go to many places. It will shock you but we have visited places on Earth, places so distant that it would take us years to travel there."

The group of old men started to talk among themselves. "Impossible." "Witchcraft, surely, it is the only explanation."

Leandor spoke, his ancient face quivering in fear. "What you say is not possible, young Psorsis. Surely not even your great-grandfather Psorsis had such powers."

"Ah, but it *is* possible." Kristiana strode through the crowd, her face now level with the old man's. "Would it surprise you to learn, Leandor, that we have gone even further? That we have left this planet? That we have travelled through the darkness of space itself and have seen many wonders?" The old men began to clamour loudly. Kristiana raised her voice to be heard. "It is true! You will believe me, your leader!" They heard this, and fell silent.

"I have more to say. This power which my grandfather has given to us allows even more. In this chamber I saw the destruction of our own people of Atlantis! Our ancestors!" Her voice quivered as she recounted what she had seen. "I saw the great cities of Atlantis shrivel in a fire so intense that it melted the very stones. I watched as the continent split into a hundred pieces and the sea washed over it all, obliterating everything in its path. Millions of our ancestors died in that holocaust. And I saw them die."

Now her voice became angry. "But I will tell you another thing. A fact which even I cannot fathom. The destruction of our people was intentional." The group became quiet, waiting for her to speak.

"You have heard the tale. That the destruction of Atlantis was caused by a comet which hurtled through the heavens, striking at the very heart of our civilisation. Now I know the truth. A force of great power turned that comet against us. For some reason unknown to us, the civilisation of Atlantis was intentionally destroyed. We were hunted down just as we hunt the deer which graze through our valley. I do not know why, but it is true."

She looked at the group of elders, now frozen in fear. "You have every reason to be afraid. What has happened before may happen again. I have told you this because I need your counsel." Slowly, she sat down on the quartz dais. "Together, we will decide how to protect ourselves and the lives of our children."

For the rest of the day, and far into the night, the elders gave counsel. Some believed that they had no option. The Atlantean people should remain in the Place of the Sun. Others felt that they should move immediately, trekking east in search of other lands in which they might settle. Kristiana listened carefully, taking note of all that they said.

In the end, it was the ancient Leandor who made the best proposal. "We cannot fight what we cannot see," he said quietly. "Would it not be best to create outposts? Places where we might look toward the heavens? Then, if we saw destruction approaching, we might prepare to avoid it."

Kristiana thought about this, her face almost hidden behind her hair. At last, she rose from the dais. "What Leandor says is true. From this moment on, we shall prepare for the coming battle."

Devising the plan was simple enough; executing it was more difficult. Initially, Kristiana had considered placing her people in many locations throughout the solar system. With the power of the chamber, transporting groups of Atlantean warriors to distant worlds would be simple. From these locations, they could scan the cosmos and give warning if anything suspicious were seen.

With this in mind, Kristiana visited each of the other eight worlds in the sun's system. What she saw made her realise that her plan was unworkable. The planets closest to the sun were too hot, their atmosphere inhospitable. She scanned these quickly and moved on.

The furthest planets were similarly inappropriate. The gaseous composition of the larger planets, while beautiful to view, would be unable to support man. For many hours she stood on the quartz dais, the swirling clouds of a gaseous giant hovering on the chamber ceiling above her, or she would glide along the multi-coloured rings of another world, contemplating the million fragments of ice and rock that made up the intricate series of circles.

Her last hope had been the red planet, one of their closest celestial neighbours. As she approached it, she saw the beautiful reds and yellows, and detected the haze of atmosphere. Nowhere, however, could she find life. She knew that here men would die if exposed on this barren world.

Having found no habitable world, she abandoned the idea.

Her next option was to use the chamber as the means for detection. She knew that for this to be effective, they must keep watch constantly and if they were to do this, the chamber could be used for no other purpose than as an observation post. Kristiana considered this option and rejected it. She was determined that the chamber should be used to advance her people's knowledge. She did not know how long their observations might go on. They could be searching for a potential enemy for years. She would have to find a different way.

The answer came to her from her grandfather, through the scrolls themselves. While Kristiana's years of study of the scrolls had allowed her to manipulate the power beneath the Earth, certain sections of Psorsis's mathematics were still abstruse – the relationships between sections as yet unfathomable. It would take many years of further study to unlock all the secrets that lay in the glass-enclosed pages.

One such section intrigued her, however. One of the scrolls indicated that it might be possible to erect huge barriers of energy around specific objects. The notes indicated that such barriers were the product of enhanced light, to be emitted by a specific, focused energy source. Psorsis believed that such a barrier would ultimately defend Atlantis from any attack.

Kristiana studied the mathematics intently. In them could be the key to a permanent solution. If she could develop such a shield, it could defend her civilisation against any attack. The concepts were difficult and tested the limits of her knowledge. At last she found the answer but what she found disappointed her.

To develop such a barrier of energy was possible. The problem lay in the source of that energy. Her mathematical calculations indicated that the power necessary for such a barrier was phenomenal. She could only guess at the amount required. In any case, she believed it to be far in excess of that available to her, even if she could somehow tap the entire potential energy which lay beneath the dais of the chamber.

A theoretical solution to the energy problem was at hand, of course. Every day, the sun poured incredible energy on to the surface of the Earth. If she could tap into that energy and direct it . . . certainly, then she would have a composite force necessary to do what was needed. The question was how.

She talked to her son and together they formulated a plan. It called for further modification of the chamber, and certain reconstruction of the exterior of the monument. They called in the engineer, Torman, who had so diligently constructed the chamber. Torman, son of Torcas, had learned many things from his father. He had applied this knowledge well, and Kristiana now entrusted him with his greatest task. Showing him the plans, she asked if it might be accomplished. He studied the plans keenly. At last he turned to her, saying, "Yes, it can be done."

The project took over a year. The quartz at the front of the monument was dismantled, and each of the individual quartz stones examined. More than half of the thousands of stones were rejected as impure and unsuitable. Many journeys were undertaken by gatherers and engineers to the shale valley, there to find appropriate replacements. The entire façade was then reconstructed. It was done with a mathematical precision dictated by Kristiana.

Next, the rear of the chamber was excavated. A tunnel, almost a replica of the front entrance, was carved through the huge stone blocks. Tonnes of rubble were hauled by hand, up and out of the monument. When this was completed, the new entrance was covered by a large section of rock, and the whorls and diamonds – the symbols of the power of the monument – were carved carefully upon it.

The most critical element of the reconstruction came last. Working closely with Torman, Kristiana selected the purest pieces of quartz, so pure as to be almost clear crystal. These were erected at the end of the front-entrance shaft, directly above the quartz dais of the chamber. A vertical shaft was then bored directly through the ceiling. The placement of the quartz pieces, their angular alignment, and the alignment of both entrances was critical to Kristiana's calculations. For many days, she worked closely with Torman, making final adjustments, to ensure that all was perfect. At last she was satisfied.

When the construction was complete, Kristiana finally turned her attention to the quartz dais. Her calculations indicated that the mass of the dais was not sufficient for the power that it must control, its crystalline characteristics inappropriate to focus the fantastic forces which she believed would be generated. She knew that she must replace the dais.

Her men scattered throughout the countryside, looking for a quality of crystal not yet encountered. Many times, Kristiana was called to a distant excavation site, her sweating men praying that the crystal which they had spent hours uncovering would be appropriate. She rejected all that she surveyed.

Finally, she was called south, back to the shale valley, the original quarry which Midreas had mined. There, a young engineer, working by himself, had unearthed a huge crystalline block. Upon hearing of the discovery, Kristiana went to it immediately. The youth stood by her, sweat dripping from his chest and arms, as he waited for her decision. Critically, she examined the crystalline block. She rose, nodding approval.

Her men worked as never before, transporting the heavy block through mountains and across the sea, finally making their way up from the floor of the Place of the Sun to the monument. At last, the block was lowered through the newly constructed shaft, down into the chamber. Torman, Psorsis and a group of engineers waited below, guiding the new block at last to its resting place. The clarity of the new dais was dazzling. Finally, they carved a large crevasse into its crystalline structure. Within this would sit the scrolls of Psorsis, their glass composition providing the final focal point required for the control of the massive energy. When this was completed, the scrolls were inserted. And now, the monument was ready – ready to unleash a new power, a brilliant energy; only waiting for the will of Kristiana to release its potential.

Kristiana made certain that all had been prepared. She looked once again at her calculations. She marvelled that her predecessor, Midreas, had the foresight to design the monument as he did. It was as if, even then, he had anticipated the needs of his niece. Now, his postulates would be combined with the knowledge of his father Psorsis, and the control and understanding of Kristiana to create a power never before seen on Earth.

It was raining. As she had done many years ago with Rengal, Kristiana rose early on this shortest day of the year, trudging wearily up the slope from her sleeping hut, up along the muddy trail. Torman and her son were with her. The rest of her people had been evacuated from the area, down to the rubble of their old, abandoned village. Kristiana paused at the entrance to the monument, looking down towards the river which flowed through the valley. From there, she could just make out the early morning smoke from the huge encampment which her fellow citizens had made. The evacuation was a hardship, she knew. But she also knew that if her mathematics were incorrect, the results could be devastating. She would regret the death of her son, and even of Torman, but she could not see the purpose in killing them all if it went wrong.

It was, however, a risk worth taking. The forces which she hoped to generate would yield a great barrier of power, a barrier which would surround the Earth, protecting it. This, she hoped, would give them the defensive protection which they needed from whatever intelligent entity had destroyed the ancient Atlantean civilisation. She stood for a moment, savouring the early morning air. Soon, the sun would rise. She nodded to Psorsis and Torman. "Let us go in," she said.

She stood on the dais, waiting. Above her, Torman also waited. He squatted in front of the entrance to the monument, waiting for the first rays of light which would herald the dawn of the winter sun. The rain had stopped, the clouds clearing away to the south. She heard Torman scramble across the rough stones above her. "It's coming," he gasped sharply. "I will leave you now."

"Yes," she called up to him. "Stand well away from the monument. Make certain that you keep clear of both entrances."

Psorsis stood behind her, waiting. She looked at him, eager, ready. "Well, my son," she said. "Shall we see what your great-grandfather dreamed of?" She turned from him, and raised her arms.

The room darkened. The forces from below brightened suddenly, the immense power manifested itself, soaking the room in a hellish red light. For a moment, they could hear the powers of the secret rivers, the thunder of fire acting against water, and then the room went black as Kristiana used her mind to control the forces of nature, to focus them in the dais.

Now the crystal block began to condense its power. Twice as large as the old dais, it pulsated, gaining energy, storing the power which gave the chamber its primary focus. Its crystalline structure was visible in the pulsating light, and then it grew so bright that Psorsis could no longer look. His mother was lost in an aurora of light and power, and yet he knew that she stood, ready, waiting, controlling the power that lay beneath them.

He heard a shout of warning from above. The sun was rising. Slowly, the great sphere rose over the hills, its light soaking the top of the valley in a blood-red display. The top of the monument became bathed in light, which gradually moved down towards the entrance as the sun continued to rise. Now, the quartz façade began to sparkle in the light. On the shortest day of the year, the relationship between the silica pieces, as established by Kristiana, was perfect. As they absorbed the sun's energy, they too began to pulsate with power, reflecting the light, bouncing it back and forth among the stones, tossing it, moulding it, focusing it on its single purpose. The wall of quartz began to glow, ruddy red at first, and then brighter, brighter, a wall of brilliant pinpricks of light, now forming a single focus of energy.

Below, Kristiana felt the surging force but it was not yet enough. The sun rose further until it was clear of the hill, casting its energy directly onto the quartz façade. Its bright, clear light penetrated the front entrance tunnel, working back all the way to the new wall of energy-hoarding quartz. This quartz, too, warmed, absorbing the great power which played on its surface. The quartz glowed brighter than the sun, brighter than anything which man had seen. Kristiana waited, the power below kept at bay, the forces above her not yet ready.

Now, the time had come. Kristiana opened her mind, releasing the energies that surged around her.

The quartz released the energy that it had absorbed. A strip of light, white hot, shot down the entrance tunnel, combining with the energy that lay trapped in the quartz above her. This, too, she now released. Pure white energy, focused and controlled by Kristiana, bolted from the ceiling of the chamber, down through the vertical shaft, directly through her, combining with the power which she controlled in the dais. The dais sparkled as if alive, energy bouncing through the chamber, playing through Kristiana, her body distorted from the power that she held, shimmering, translucent. The great forces of nature, there, surrounding her, roaring like a hurricane, becoming part of her, consuming the chamber with its unyielding, yet controlled, energy.

A beam of light, as bright as a thousand bolts of lightning, broke from the back entrance to the chamber. It rose, up, through the sun-enriched atmosphere, up and out, directed by Kristiana, coming at last to its prime position, spreading now, like a ghostly vapour, a curtain moving swiftly around the planet. Nothing was in its way to break the curtain, and if there had been anything, it would have been destroyed. It tested that power once. A meteorite, captured by the gravity of the Earth long ago, made its way toward the atmosphere. It encountered the moving blanket of energy and instantly disintegrated, fine fragments glowing for a minute in intense heat before they vaporised.

Psorsis helped his mother from the dais. He looked at her carefully, noting that her skin still glowed with energy, her body shimmering with the remnants of the power which she had controlled. Exhausted by her efforts, she slumped against him. Slowly, she brought her face to his, her eyes searching his own. "We have done what Psorsis has taught us. Let us go to see if his teachings have saved our people."

Slowly, they climbed from the chamber. The sky was clear, rainwater sparkling in the morning sun. Kristiana and Psorsis looked up. Above them, as fine as gossamer, a golden network sparkled, an intricate cobweb of moving light, moving ghostlike for as far as they could see.

For the first time in many months, Kristiana felt at peace. Perhaps now, the vision which she had seen of the destruction of Atlantis would leave her and they could live without fear.

They were not yet gods, though some of them had dreamed of becoming so. Millions of years ago, their ancestors had developed out of the slime of a planet which orbited around a blue-white star, not unlike Earth's. For the next few thousand years, they copulated, sending their teaming billions to move about the face of their planet, growing, learning. Attempting to overcome their carbon-based environment so that they could live and multiply. And as with many cultures, they made war and peace. Many individual entities died. Whole localised civilisations were buried in the storms of hatred and aggression which were characteristic of their species. Yet somehow, they flourished.

They called themselves naKuna, the People. As they matured, those individuals who possessed traits of intelligence moved to the forefront of their society. These espoused peace. Development.

Kindness. Nurturing. They argued passionately that survival and growth of their species could be accomplished only by putting aside the elements of fear and hatred which were also part of their being. Their arguments swayed a population which had grown weary of war. And so it happened that the occupants of the planet chose to follow a path of enlightenment. For the most part, their feelings of envy, hatred and loathing were vanquished.

With this development, this race advanced quickly. They channelled all of their energies into the advancement of their society and their individual characteristics. For the next few thousand years, they raced towards technological genius. They entered the age of the machine – and their machines became some of the most powerful and constructive in all the universe.

Having conquered their world, their gaze moved towards the stars. With their machines, they travelled effortlessly within the localised star system. As they did, they discovered – not so surprisingly – that they were not the only intelligent beings in the universe. Where they discovered life, they did what they could to protect it. To nurture it. For their culture now understood that life, in whatever form, was only an accident of universal development. And for that reason, this culture chose to protect all life for it understood just how precious life was. This became the primary mission for their living, and for their continued growth.

For that reason, the age of the machine ended. As their intellects developed further, this culture found that machines only impeded their ability to seek out new forms of life. Machines were only as effective as the sum of their parts, no matter from what materials those parts were manufactured. As this culture sought new life-forms to nurture, it found that machines limited travel. And travel was now its primary modus. naKuna had already located and isolated all life-forms in their part of the known universe. Yet they knew that there were thousands – no, millions – of galaxies yet to discover and explore. Machines would never allow them to accomplish this task.

For this reason, naKuna looked at other alternatives. Some elements split off from the main group of their culture, renouncing their physical bodies and moving their being into the complex structure of enzymes which circled through the galaxies. Other elements transported themselves into radio waves, joining with the songs which the universe had uttered since its violent birth so many aeons ago.

Another group devolved into the properties of light, moving throughout the universe, bending in the great magnetic fields of suns and planetary fields.

All of them, no matter of what form, sought knowledge and life throughout the universe. They sought to propagate every nook and cranny with beacons of intelligence. And through this, they believed that they would come to know true fulfilment.

Of their number, one rebelled at its mission. Within itself, buried in the genetic coding which made up its life's characteristics, were the haunting remnants of naKuna's bleak and tumultuous past. Here, envy resided. Jealousy and hatred thrived. It cared not for nurturing other forms of life. Rather, It sought to protect Its own self-interest. And while Its brethren moved throughout the universe to provide nurture, It chose instead to undermine that very precept of its culture. It would choose instead to use Its powers to destroy.

When naKuna discovered that a deviant resided in their midst, they tried for a thousand years to persuade It to adopt tolerance and forbearance. But this warped creature would know no love. With reluctance, naKuna chose then to banish It from their fellowship. On a current of pure energy, they transported this dark element of their own being to a far corner of the universe. To a place which they had not yet explored. Which, they believed, held no life-forms. And there It would reside in a vacuum. Neutralised, yet unchecked. An evil which would project Its feelings of unworthiness through unthinking destruction.

16

The attack upon what men now call Earth was not the first of Its atrocities. For many millions of years, It had stayed in this corner of the universe. When It detected life-forms of any type, It saw a threat to Its own existence. Believing that new life, in thriving, might banish It as had Its brothers and sisters, the enmity contained within Its soul shouted for destruction. Using the powers which were a part of Its being, It moved to comply with Its terrible mission. Again and again, It showered young civilisations with the fires of hell until this part of the universe knew only a barrenness and stagnation.

When It had discovered the life-form which men called Atlantis, It sought to destroy this with as little thought as any of Its previous murders. In the years since the initial attack, It had observed that planet with indifference. The comet which It had chosen so carefully was large enough for Its purpose. Had It desired, It could have destroyed the planet at will. But the planet held promise for other activities. Perhaps It could one day use it to breed children in Its own likeness. But for now, the planet must be cleansed. Rather than turn the blue and white globe into rubble, It had chosen instead this simple compromise.

Its mind was powerful. In Its power and inexhaustible ego, It determined that only a relatively small force was required. It found the method for destruction easily enough. The comet, a little larger than a small moon, tumbled through space on its relentless orbit around the small, yellow companion sun. Skilfully, It cast Its intelligence into the vacuum, first capturing the magnetic fields which coiled through space, drawing them together, directing them carefully on the ancient rock which moved silently around the sun. The vortex of energy now formed, the entity which the people of Atlantis called Borgnoff interrupted that eternal orbit, changing it as easily as a child might change the course of a rolling marble.

The cities of the continent provided a perfect target. The comet, controlled by the magnetic vortex that It had caused, moved perfectly. The outer atmosphere caused it little trouble. The impact was as planned, the Earth swallowed first by fire, then by the raging forces of the planet's oceans as they filled the floundering and torn continent. For a moment, It felt the joy of the executioner. It had removed what could have one day been a threat to Its great unyielding destiny, a destiny which would not let any other intelligence stand in its way. Turning Its back on the smoking rubble of the continent, It moved – as It always did – in search of new colonies to destroy. Still, It was careful to leave behind the slave scout. Its primitive consciousness would note the results of the destruction, and would report back if it sensed anything unusual. As the creature left the system of nine planets, It believed that the scout would remain silent for ever more.

For many years, the entity called Borgnoff forgot the scout as It searched for new cultures to destroy. Then, the unexpected happened. From the other side of the universe, the intelligence heard the faint cry of its look-out.

For generations the scout had maintained its orbit high above the planet of blues and whites. Nothing disturbed it, so it had no cause to act. Then it noted a field of pure energy which bore up and over the planet. It monitored this, and now it moved to respond as it had been instructed long ago. It noted the initial source of the power, its strength, its intent. Silently, it communicated its finding to its distant master. Annoyed, the intelligence which had turned away from this planet so long ago now turned back once again. This time, It would make certain that Its work was complete.

The attack came much more quickly than Kristiana had anticipated. It was raining, the wind howling through the valley, the villagers hastening along the muddy paths. The sky was a dirty grey, clouds scudding low along the horizon, enveloping the Atlanteans in a fine mist. This early spring afternoon was a day to huddle indoors next to an open fire.

The light came without warning, brilliant white, flaring through the dark clouds, brighter than a lightning flash. For a moment, the village stood fixed in its intensity, each hut, each blade of grass, each individual rock captured in its grasp. Animals and men who turned their startled gaze toward its origin would never see again, their corneas obliterated by the blinding flash. They were the lucky ones.

The heat was intense. The rain-wet wood of the huts smoked, quickly drying. The thin wattle came alive, then, burst into flame. Throughout the village, fires raged, men and women running quickly, trying to save their homes.

Men caught outside were burned in the intense heat, their hair seared, their skin mottled black and red, blistered by the fire that had come from the heavens. Some died instantly, their bodies scattered throughout the village, face down in the mud, their wool clothes still smouldering. Others lay nearby, weeping with the intense pain. Cries of anguish echoed throughout the village.

As suddenly as the light came, it went. Panic gripped the village, members of the tribe running like stricken deer to hiding places, gathering their families together, leading the newly-blinded and the burned, stumbling up the slippery path into the overgrowth, looking for protection.

Kristiana had been more fortunate. That afternoon, she had chosen to work in the monument, poring over the scrolls for new secrets which would help her to thwart any threat. She did not see the light, nor hear the roar of heat as it swept through the atmosphere towards the village.

"Mother." She heard his call, and turned from her studies. Psorsis came down the dark steps, clothing burned, his exposed skin a mottle of blisters. She went to him quickly, holding him, gently lowering her son to the stone floor.

"What . . . ?"

"The village . . . " He gasped for air. She eased his singed hair away from the burnt face.

"Tell me," she said simply.

He told her of the attack then, his words tumbling thickly from his parched throat. "Luck was with you," he said. "Our people have scattered into the valley, seeking shelter. They're terrified. I counted well over fifty people blinded by the light, and many others have been burnt to death. It is fortunate that we do not have more casualties." Kristiana sat on the ground by him, the light of the quartz dancing over her face. Then she rose quickly.

"You have seen to the rest of the tribe?" she asked.

"Yes. I have men out looking for our people. I have ordered them to bring all the tribe back to the village." He looked at her, sweat on his face. "Any of the elders who have not been injured are seeing to the casualties. I do not think that our situation is critical." He looked away, suddenly uncertain. "But they asked me to give you a message. They ask what you will do." He paused, looking uneasily at this mother. "It is, I take it, what you feared?"

She rose from the desk, considering. "I'm unsure. It could have been many things. Perhaps a large meteor striking the great barrier which we've erected. But it seems unlikely." Quickly, gathering the pages from the scrolls, she returned them to their glass enclosure. "Come," she said. "We must be certain."

The sun and its nine planets, orbiting relentlessly, floated above them, silently moving across the ink-black surface of the chamber. Kristiana stood on the quartz dais, composed, aware, controlling the raging forces beneath her. The chamber was quiet, mute, its serenity contrasting starkly with the burning village which lay in ruins outside the monument.

From their position, the sun and its children looked as they always had. They moved undisturbed, spinning through the timeless vacuum. Vainly, Kristiana and Psorsis searched for the origins of the light. Nowhere could they see any disturbance.

Kristiana moved them, then, towards their own planet. The blue and white globe floated directly above them, its swirling masses of clouds moving relentlessly over the great seas. Here, however, was a difference. The immense surface of their home planet was covered by a transient gossamer of golden lace which shifted and rippled, now almost solid, the next moment invisible. Along its tenuous strands, beads of pure white light moved quickly from one nexus to the other, like drops of water falling down a spider's web. The great barrier which Kristiana had put into place still glistened, its power seemingly undisturbed.

"Whatever fell on us has not damaged the barrier significantly."

"Perhaps it was as you said. A natural occurrence. Something fell on to the barrier. The flash of light, the heat, were only by-products of its destruction."

Kristiana was unsure. "If it was natural, it was precise. That it struck directly above our village is certainly more than a coincidence. We must know."

Kristiana concentrated, tapping the power surrounding her, focusing the energies of her world, adapting them to her will. Above them, the spinning of Earth slowed, then stopped. For a moment Kristiana paused; then her mind moved backwards and, as it did, Earth moved again, a shimmering orb caught on a background of the blackest velvet. Now, as they watched, time itself moved backwards.

The comet had come from deep space, the orbit which it had known for aeons. As they watched, the vacuum which surrounded it flexed, bending, ripples of energy forming a vortex, with its centre the grey-white fragment of rock which was the quiescent comet. They watched as the comet turned, controlled by the vortex. Now, it encountered the gravity of the sun, the magnetic field controlling it, bringing it closer. Quickly, it moved past the outer planets, brightening as it absorbed the sun's power. It glowed, the outer particles of the comet turning into gasses, thrown off into space, pouring its incandescent trail into the vacuum.

For a moment, it seemed to hang over Earth, pausing as if considering its next move. Then, it plunged toward the surface with intelligent purpose. Light flooded the chamber with its brilliance, pouring on them but impotent to harm them. The golden web of the barrier burned white with the energy of the impact, absorbing it, dissipating it, consuming the object that had caused it.

"Now, we know." Kristiana breathed quickly, her pupils dilated with fear. Her son stood quietly by the dais.

"But the barrier held."

Kristiana looked at her son. "But for how long, Psorsis? Can it withstand a prolonged attack? Can our people survive many bombardments?"

Psorsis shook his head. "Certainly, whatever controls the comet must have seen the result of their work. Surely, they will not continue."

"Will they not? Look."

Above them, the sun moved along its orbit, as it had always moved. Its children floated peacefully, blanketed by the blackness of eternal night. As they watched, the blackness became filled by hundreds of lights, bright motes moving relentlessly across the ebony darkness of the universe.

Kristiana spoke then, simply, to her son. "It is Borgnoff come again." She turned to him. "Call the elders to me, Psorsis. Quickly." While Psorsis ran to carry out his mother's orders, Kristiana watched the faint motes of light glow brighter as they moved silently towards her.

With the elders once again before her, Kristiana outlined what must be done. If they were to save themselves, they must leave. Not only the village. No, they must leave the planet of their birth if the Atlantean culture was to survive.

At first, the elders of her tribe argued, stating that her plan was too risky. It was one thing, they said, to flee on foot across a familiar landscape. It was another to throw their entire culture across the infinity of space.

Kristiana listened to their arguments but she held her ground, as certain as her grandfather Psorsis had been when he recommended the evacuation of the great Atlantis. Carefully, she listened to her elders, letting them air their opinions, allowing the panic in their voices to subside. Standing on the dais, at last she spoke.

"Many years ago, the great Psorsis, my son's great-grandfather, argued that our people should leave Atlantis in order to protect our culture. Now we must do the same again. We must remember that with which we have been charged: the preservation of our race, of our culture. That and that alone is our only task. It is why we live and work."

She stood regally, her white gown falling upon the opaque whiteness of the quartz dais. She continued. "I have listened to your arguments, but they are without substance. Even with the powers which we have at our disposal, that which has unleashed this attack towards us is unyielding. Even if the barrier of power above us does hold, it cannot protect us entirely from such an onslaught. To do nothing is to spell the end of our people."

In the end, they agreed with her. The facts which she brought before them were indisputable. They moved quickly to act.

The elders assembled the people. Almost a thousand people, men, women, and children, clutched the few personal belongings which were allowed to them. The injured and the old were carried gently. While these made their way to the monument, others on the orders of Kristiana continued to search the surrounding countryside for the many who had fled. They would leave no one behind to face the destruction which would come from the skies. Yet she knew that some – a handful – would refuse to leave. And she knew that, in some ways, this was good. If they survived, Atlantis would continue on this planet, even if it would never again grow to its former greatness.

As they moved up towards the monument, Kristiana worked intently. With her son beside her, she reviewed the many explorations of the universe which they had undertaken. She remembered one particular world: a place of three suns with mighty oceans and lush vegetation. Great fish swam in its seas and on the land huge lumbering beasts grazed on grasses reflecting the red light of the largest sun. On this world, the world of the Red Giant sun, the Atlanteans might yet survive.

The evacuation began just as the next wave of brilliant light burned through the dark clouds which still hung above the village. Many more people were mutilated horribly in the rain of fire, and the remnants of their village now lay smouldering.

For the last time, Kristiana stood on the quartz dais. Above her, the world of the three suns hung, its brilliant blues and whites reminding her of the Earth they were leaving. Around her, a hundred of her people stood in the chamber, waiting. She was conscious of the others of her tribe waiting in the tunnels or standing at the entrance to the monument, waiting for the moment when they could leave the terrible tumult that flashed down at them from the heavens.

She drove her mind as never before, bringing the world above her closer, filling the chamber. Now, she hurtled over a great sea, and in the distance, she saw the white cliffs and hills of land. Along its edge, she could make out the lush greens of vegetation. Here, she would send her people.

She turned, now, looking for her son. She put out her hand to him, and Psorsis stepped up on the dais with her. She required his energy, his intelligence, if she were to complete the task. With him, she concentrated yet again. Above them the planet came alive, the sounds of its being crashing through the chamber, its atmosphere charged with fear. Kristiana, with Psorsis, reached up, up into the vision above and now she became a part of that vision; they were a living tunnel between one world and the next. And along this path, their people walked.

They went quickly, moving across the chamber floor, up on to the dais, stepping through the shimmering forms that bridged a great gulf. As they moved across this shining path, Kristiana felt herself become one with the great energy which she controlled. She felt herself slipping, her mind moving away from her body, and she clung on, knowing that she must hold if she were to save the people.

With all but a few safely through to the other side, Kristiana had one final task. As she held the door to their survival open, four of her strongest men reached beneath her and Psorsis, lifting the scrolls reverently from their resting place. They glowed, the energy from the great powers beneath them flowing through them, focusing, the glowing forces then moving into the transparent figure that was the living bridge of Kristiana. The glass of the scrolls shimmering with its power, now reflected the light of the new world above it. The carriers moved up on to the huge dais, and with the scrolls moved across the void, taking the translucent figures of Kristiana and her son with them, walking from their old world to the new.

For now, at least, the culture of Atlantis would survive.

It watched impassively as the attack continued. For twenty solar days, the planet was pummelled by the great masses of ancient rock, moved precisely toward the target beneath it. With all of Its intelligence, It could not understand the golden latticework of light which inhibited the torrent of destruction. With each attack, however, the barrier of energy grew weaker, its shimmering surface dissipating beneath the hammer blows which it suffered. Still, it refused to yield, protecting that which was beneath from direct impact.

When the last comet had lit the sky with brilliance, It waited for the land to cool. Finally, It moved through the vacuum, Its energy bright in the conviction that It had won.

The attack had been concentrated and for miles around the target the land lay barren, still smoking. All living things had been consumed in the heat that had rained from the sky. But despite the destruction, the intelligence was puzzled. It had expected to find a great civilisation, now crumbled into waste. Instead, only a few cinders lay smouldering, the remnants of a poor, undeveloped culture.

The thing that was Borgnoff probed into the rubble, looking for the society which had fashioned the shield of energy, the barrier which had protected the planet from the worst of the onslaught. It found nothing in the remnants of the wooden structures, now only smears of burned carbon lying on a muddy ground.

It examined carefully the great stone and earth mound which rose beside the smoking village. It had suffered greatly in the attack. The white stone facing had collapsed, covering the front entrance completely, and a number of huge rock plinths rested on their sides, uprooted from the soil.

Its mind entered the mound, searching for the intelligence which It knew It must find. The room, buried beneath a great mass of fallen rubble, was empty. Here, however, It felt power, moving restlessly. Power which had been harnessed and employed with skill. Smelling Its quarry, It searched, but nowhere could It find the users of that power. That intelligence was gone.

Enraged that It had been thwarted, It moved again away from the planet. For the briefest of moments, It thought of destroying the planet completely. But it was no longer a threat. Like a lion ignoring its dead quarry, It looked now for other game. But It would not forget. Somewhere, that which had eluded It still survived. Borgnoff would remember. And some day, the hunter would hunt again.

They were not omniscient. As with any advancing civilisation, they had limitations which included simple physics. However, naKuna, the People, had methods of monitoring activity even in the remotest regions of the universe.

The disruption in gravity fields caused by various inter-stellar conflagrations were recorded, catalogued and analysed by the sensors that had been placed far afield. Initially, these outbursts seemed no more unusual than the birth of a new star or the appearance of a nova – or the destruction of a comet.

As they plotted these activities, they noted the co-ordinates and frequencies of these outbursts. Through such an analysis, they hoped eventually to understand the very secrets of universal growth and evolution. It was with some surprise, therefore, that they noted the frequency with which these outbursts were occurring in a remote segment of a little – explored stellar corner. Galactic outbursts in this area ran far above normative frequencies.

The alarm was only raised, however, when it was realised that it was to this remote region that their dark, dysfunctional brethren had been expelled. naKuna understood, then. In their desire to isolate evil, they had inadvertently imperilled other civilisations. In their deep appreciation for life, they decided to take action. And in that moment, a single element of their kind was despatched to neutralise that which they had thought to be impotent.

PART TWO

Brave New Worlds

17

"For God's sake, Barnabus, don't just stand there! Run for it!" Jonathan grabbed Barnabus by the sleeve of his overcoat, pulling the teacher roughly away from the field. He carried the laptop computer in his other hand. Cathy followed, dragging the suitcase and briefcase. Above them, the silent shafts of white light moved freely. Where they touched the slender golden buildings, the metal crumbled, turning into molten streams. Smoke curled lazily up from the floor of the city.

Barnabus ran, trying to take in the strange world around him. "You would have thought that we would get a proper welcome."

Jonathan tugged the teacher forward. "I don't think they had time, Barnabus. Would you hurry up, for God's sake?" He looked behind him. Fingers of smoking energy streaked towards them. Where they touched the ground, the earth shuddered, spitting melted fragments and smoke into the air. Cathy lagged behind, struggling with the suitcase. "Hurry up, will you, Cathy? You've got an electrical welcoming committee right behind you."

She turned briefly, seeing the forces behind her, scorching the land. She stumbled, hiked the suitcase higher and ran.

Jonathan saw the ruin of a building in front of him. He pointed to it. "Over there. Come on, let's get in out of this." He charged towards the structure, Barnabus tailing behind him. The field behind them exploded into a million pieces, the fingers of light relentlessly coming towards them. At last he reached the walls of the building. Finding a gap in the masonry, he moved quickly, climbing through, pulling Barnabus in behind him. Cathy dived in after him.

Jonathan looked out. The arcs of brilliant light had stopped moving towards them. As he watched, they moved away, hunting, liquidating everything in their path.

"Phew!" He shook his head, moving back into the safety of the wrecked building, and sat with his back against the wall. He rested for a second, head between his legs. He looked up at Barnabus. The teacher was sitting on a lump of metal. "Hey, Barnabus, I hate to say anything, but I think maybe we came to the wrong place . . . "

Cathy, slumped against the wall, nodded. "Somehow, I don't think that you had this in mind. Certainly, they must have gone somewhere else."

Barnabus was calmly wiping his glasses with an old handkerchief. "Impossible. Quite impossible. They're here somewhere. You can be certain of that."

"Sure. And those things . . . " Jonathan pointed out the door, " . . . those were the neighbours greeting us in warm welcome." He got to his feet, walking over to the teacher. "For God's sake, Barnabus, this place *can't* be right. It's raining destruction all over. You must have made a mistake."

"Sorry, lad, sorry. But you're wrong. This is it. I'm certain." He looked across at Cathy. "You both saw the whorl on the ceiling of Newgrange. You know that we tracked toward it. And might I remind you that we've carefully studied all other planets in this system? This was the only world capable of supporting life. The ancients from Newgrange *must* have come here."

Cathy stood up. "Fine. So maybe they did come here. But something tells me that they're not here now." She stared at both of them. "Whether they're here or not seems to be beside the point. As Jonathan has pointed out, it's hailing fire outside. I think we should give up this search of yours, Barnabus, and get out of here. Right now."

Her teacher looked up at her, startled. "Now? You want to

leave now? But we've only just arrived!"

"Barnabus, didn't you see . . . "

"Yes, I saw!" He rose, facing them. "Have you forgotten? We're on a new world. A new planet! It's fascinating! A world revolving around three suns. With cities which, I believe, are made from the purest gold! Certainly, you must find this of interest."

"I'm only interested in going home."

"Jesus, Barnabus. This isn't a giant classroom." Jonathan walked over to the teacher. "Hasn't it crossed your mind that maybe, just maybe, we could get killed if we stayed here?"

"Yes, but . . . "

"No buts, Barnabus." Cathy whirled toward him, her expression icy. "Are you going to get us out of here or not?"

"Ah. Yes, well . . . " He paused, a blank look on his moustached face. "We have only one small problem."

"Only one problem. I'd say we've got more than one. But go on, what is it?"

"Ahhhh, well you see, we can't go back. At least not right now."

"Whaat?" Jonathan stared hard at his teacher. "What did you say?"

"It's true, I'm afraid."

"Why?"

"We don't have the power source to re-connect with Earth."

Jonathan pointed to the briefcase. "But what about all that stuff in there? All that electrical garbage?"

"Spares, mostly, I'm afraid. I don't know really why I brought them. I thought I might use them."

"So you . . . you brought us here, knowing that we couldn't get back again?" Cathy's face was white.

"No, not exactly. I figured that we would meet the makers of the transport system which we have used so effectively. I thought that they would have a similar system. Then, simple! We just use that one to get back home again."

"You thought. *You thought*! Of all the crazy, bizarre . . . " Jonathan turned, tramping towards the doorway. "And what

141

about that out there? Those little bits of high voltage body-warmers? What about those, huh?"

Barnabus looked at the floor glumly. "I don't know, Jonathan. I just don't know."

"Great! Just great!" Jonathan stormed to the far wall, leaning his head against the still-warm metal.

Cathy turned to him. "So what does that mean? We're trapped here?"

Barnabus sighed. "Apparently. Until we find the makers of Newgrange. Surely they can get us out of here and on our way home."

"And until then?"

Barnabus shook his head uncertainly. Jonathan turned slowly from the wall, facing them. He glanced at Cathy. "Until then, we're just going to have to survive."

"How?"

"I don't know yet." Jonathan walked back to the doorway. The great energy was again centred on the city, tearing it apart. He watched for a moment. "Well, we know we can't go back there." He turned slightly, surveying the area. The building they were in was in the centre of a plain which seemed to stretch out for at least two kilometres in all directions. He didn't relish the thought of running across open ground. Cautiously, he stuck his head out, looking back behind the building. He saw it then: a line of trees about two hundred metres away. And in front of the trees, a gully. He thought he saw a reflection of the red sun glinting from a stream of water.

Jonathan turned back toward Barnabus. "All right, here's what I think we should do. First, we can't stay here. God knows when those giant electrical zappers are going to come this way again. And I for one don't want to be around when they do."

"So what do you have in mind?"

"There's a stream or something behind us. We'll go there for now."

"You want me to swim in a stream?" Cathy glared at him. "That's a great idea, Jonathan, just great. Having been through the proverbial firestorm, I can now try to drown myself."

"Do you have any better ideas?" Cathy stared at him, then shook her head. "Fine. So when I say so, run like hell."

They stormed across the field, hopping over streams of molten metal that blocked their path. The gully came into view. It was full of water. Jonathan charged towards it. Behind them, the inferno intensified once again; the arcs of light, as if sensing their movement, hurtled toward them, throwing up huge plumes of debris, destroying everything in their path.

Jonathan slowed up, waiting for the others. "Come on! Run!"

"I'm running. I'm running!" Barnabus plodded over the stone field, his overcoat flopping about his pudgy waist. Cathy was right behind him.

He took Barnabus by the sleeve. The old man held his briefcase tightly. "Drop the case, for God's sake."

"No! My electronics."

"All right. But let's move!" They were at the gully. Only a metre more. The light flashed behind them. "Jump!"

Cathy and Jonathan, holding Barnabus between them, charged into the gully, sinking up to their necks in slimy water.

They stood in the ooze, trying to catch their breaths. The dangerous arcs of light suddenly stopped moving toward them, as if uncertain where their prey had gone. For a moment, blinding light ripped into the bank in front of them. They ducked, hiding beneath the surface. Jonathan held his breath for as long as he could. Finally, he surfaced, looking back along the stony plain. The electrical rain-dance had drifted away, back towards the building in which they had hidden. As he watched, the fingers of light converged on it, reducing it to a heap of molten waste.

He stood up. Beside him, Cathy tried to shake reddish-green muck from her hair. Jonathan turned to his teacher, who was, in turn, doing his best to salvage his notes from the green slime of the gully. "Now what?"

The teacher looked at them innocently. "Would it make any difference to say that I'm sorry?"

Jonathan glowered at the academic. "None whatsoever."

"So what do we do?" He turned to Cathy, at the same time holding the laptop computer well above the water line.

"Damned if I know," Cathy shrugged.

Jonathan looked again at the teacher. "You have any more ideas, Barnabus?"

Barnabus shrank a little more into the muck. "Well, actually . . . no, not at the moment." He looked down into the slime. "This does seem rather inconvenient."

"*Inconvenient!*" Jonathan slapped at the mud with both hands, splashing a mess of floating grime into his face. "Barnabus, is that all you can say? Look!" He pointed across the field at the wrecked building. "Doesn't it strike you that we're in danger?"

"Yes," Cathy said, turning to him. "We could get killed here."

"If we had stayed there, we would have been carbonised."

Barnabus thought for a moment. "Yes, well, you are right. Still . . . " The old man looked around him, " . . . we seem to be in good shape here." He looked at the muck, floating just below his chin. "Not that it's terribly comfortable."

"No, it's not comfortable. It has nothing to do with comfort." Cathy looked at him trying to keep her mouth out of the reddish-green goo. "Besides, it smells."

The old teacher breathed in deeply, then exhaled, coughing. "It does smell rather like a sewer, I'm afraid."

"Oh, God. Is that what this is?"

Jonathan groaned. "Barnabus! What Cathy is trying to say is that we've got to get out of here. But I take it that it's impossible."

Barnabus nodded glumly. "Yes, unfortunately, that is the case." He brightened. "Unless, of course, we can find the people of Newgrange."

"I hate to say this, Barnabus, but I haven't seen anybody." Jonathan looked back at the flashes of light. "And if I were living here, I certainly wouldn't come out in the open. Visitors or no visitors."

Barnabus coughed a little. "Yes. Well, you're probably right."

"Look," Cathy moved toward Jonathan, pushing the suitcase through the water, "I don't want to stop you two from your little discussion but don't you think we should *do* something?" She looked at Barnabus. He turned away from her. "Jonathan? What do you think?"

"I don't know." He stood in the water. "Maybe we should just stay here for the moment."

Cathy shook her head abruptly. "Men! You can never depend on them!" She started to wade through the stinking waters, heading toward the far bank of the gully.

"Hey! Where do you think you're going?"

She turned, glaring at Jonathan. "I don't know about you two but I'm getting out of this mess. If our only hope is to find Barnabus's ancient people, then that's what I'm going to do." She swung around, continuing toward the bank.

Jonathan shrugged. "Maybe she's right." He turned to his teacher. "Come on, Barnabus. Let's get going."

"Right. That seems to be the best." He pointed to a spot behind Jonathan. "Would you be so kind as to get the briefcase? I dropped it."

Jonathan looked. The dark brown leather top floated just above the water. "Yeah, I'll get it." He turned, wading through the muck back toward it.

"Hey. Did you see that?" Jonathan looked over his shoulder. Cathy had stopped walking. She stood, frozen to the spot, her face wooden.

"What? What did you see?"

"I don't know what I saw! I saw something all right."

"Where?"

"Don't be so stupid. Over here."

Jonathan sighed, wiping his face with his free hand. "Look, it probably wasn't anything. Just keep going, OK?"

He turned back. Then he heard her squeal. Jonathan spun around. Cathy's face had turned chalk white. "What? What did you see?"

"It was pink. I saw it. It was pink. And *big*! Oh, God."

"Where is it now?"

"There." She pointed. "No, there. It's moving. Under the water." He saw a line of bubbles then, moving away from her, out into the middle of the stream.

"Well don't just stand there. Move it!" Cathy started staggering toward the far bank. He turned to Barnabus. The academic stood rooted, looking. "Barnabus. Get moving!" The older man opened and closed his mouth a couple of times, then started slogging as fast as possible toward the far gully bank.

"Great. This is just terrific." Jonathan reached out, trying to get his hand on the briefcase. As he reached, the water around the case started to boil; streams of small bubbles played around it. Then, he saw the whirlpool. It moved under the briefcase, taking hold of it, whirling it around. He reached out, touching its top, trying to grasp it. It sank, slowly for a second, then faster, finally disappearing under the surface. He stared at the spot, then snatched his hand away. He looked around. Bubbles moved to the surface, surrounding him, belching muck into his face. He started to move then, move as fast as he could through the thick garbage floating on the water. He saw Cathy and Barnabus in front of him. Cathy was on the bank, the suitcase thrown in front of her. She was reaching down, grabbing Barnabus by the lapels of his overcoat, trying to pull him up on to dry land.

"Come on, you two, get out of the way!"

Jonathan dragged himself through the muck. He felt it, then. The waters around him began to move, a current pulling him back into the centre of the stream. He was almost to the bank now. The current became stronger, grabbing at his legs. He looked in front of him. Barnabus was halfway up the bank, his body beached like a small whale. "For God's sake, get him out of there."

Cathy looked up, frantic. "I can't. He's stuck!"

Jonathan moved as fast as he could. He was right behind Barnabus now. "Here. Take this!" He threw the laptop to

Cathy. Then, he put out his arm, placing his hand squarely in the middle of the teacher's ample posterior. "Move it, Barnabus, move it!" He pushed. The teacher grunted, and slowly pulled himself up on to the bank. The water was boiling around Jonathan. He reached out, grabbing the vegetation that grew along the riverbank. He pulled, but the vortex had him. Cathy reached out, grabbing him by the hair. She yanked as hard as she could.

Jonathan came away from the water like a cork out of a wine bottle. He tumbled to the grass, looking over his shoulder as he did. The waters in which he had just been standing were whirling now, the vortex of the small whirlpool forming, sucking in air and floating debris. As he watched, the whirlpool deepened. And now he could see a black hole forming, pink at its edges. It rose, searching. Fingers of pink wavered around the hole, moving through the muck, looking for its prey. It rose further, coming out of the water now. The huge pink fibrous trunk, as wide as a man's torso, rotated through the air. The gaping mouth at the top vomited brackish water; pink cilia as thick as fingers vibrated in vain.

It stood for a moment, seeming to sense its quarry. It struck out toward the river bank, striking the earth. It stopped, dazed, then slithered back into the waters, the reddish-green filth on the surface closing over it.

"That was close." Jonathan turned toward Cathy. "Thanks for the helping hand."

She smiled for a moment. "Hope it didn't hurt."

He rubbed his head. "Better than getting sucked into Moby Dick down there." He looked out at the stinking waters, once again calm. Then, he turned to Barnabus. "I hope those weren't your Newgrange builders. If they were, I don't think getting us home will be one of their priorities."

Barnabus sat pulling green matter out of his moustache. "No. Of course not, Jonathan. The builders of Newgrange were human. And that is what we shall find here. Human beings." He pointed to the water. "That was merely a low form of life."

"Well," Jonathan stood up, brushing his trousers. "I don't particularly want to see any other life-forms around here." He looked around. In the distance, the city was quiet. He turned. A row of trees blocked his path. "So where do we go from here?"

"As I said," Barnabus stood up, "we go to find the people who live on this planet."

"Look, Barnabus. I'm not going anywhere. You don't seem to be living in reality! We've been on this new world, or whatever you call it for, what, maybe thirty minutes? And in that time we've been almost incinerated, zapped and become a meal for old Pink Mouth back there. Anyway, you just can't be certain that men from Earth came here."

Barnabus thrust out his chin. "You're sounding insolent, Jonathan. Of course they came here. I'm certain of that." He trudged off down the line of trees, his wet overcoat flopping around his ankles.

Cathy called after him. "You don't have to run away, Barnabus. You know that Jonathan's right. You can't know for sure that men from Newgrange came here."

Barnabus stopped thirty metres down the line of trees. He paused looking through the dense foliage. Slowly, he raised his hand, pointing with a dripping finger. "Can't I?"

Jonathan and Cathy walked over to him. There, behind the trees, a huge replica of Newgrange rose above them. Many times larger than the original monument, its quartz white façade glittered in the red sunlight. In front of it, a huge block stood, apparently composed entirely of gold, its polished surface featureless. Except for a series of symbols. The great whorls of Newgrange.

18

The attack was intensifying again. As quickly as they could, the three made their way through the vegetation, hiding from time to time in the undergrowth. Overhead, the pencil-thin weapons darted, converging now on a towering building in the city centre. As they watched, it toppled in the intense heat. For a moment there was silence and then the ground shook with the impact of the structure as it hit the surface.

For a moment, there was a lull. "Come on. Let's move!" Jonathan grabbed Barnabus by the front of his soaking coat, and half dragged him across the field, toward the monument.

Now, they were at the entrance. Except for the size and composition, it was the monument at Newgrange. Giant kerbstones, manufactured entirely of metals, guarded the entrance. Huge quartz-like stones formed a magnificent wall, towering fifty metres into the air. While they stood, panting from their run, they watched as light sparked and danced, moving from one rock to the other, a part of the internal workings of the quartz itself. Jonathan looked at the others. "You ready to go inside?"

Cathy shook her head, unbelieving. "You didn't say anything about going inside, Jonathan."

"What else did you think we were going to do? Study it from out here?"

Her long hair fell in a soaking tangle about her face. "How do you know what's in there?"

The ground shook again. Fingers of light bolted from the grey clouds, destroying what they touched. Now, they moved toward them again, seeming to sense their movement, turning the earth into scorched patches of smouldering wreckage. Jonathan pointed.

"I don't care what's in there. It has to be better than what's out here."

Cathy stood for a moment, uncertain. What she saw then made her change her mind. A column of light, brighter than any they had seen, arced its way purposefully into the remnants of the golden city. For a moment, the light flickered, harmless, bathing the gold in its intensity. Now, a spectrum of current descended through the column, moving more and more rapidly, intense circles of light coalescing, playing a mindless game, becoming a part of the golden spider of buildings which they lit; now seeming to absorb the intricate web. The light circled, brighter and brighter, and the buildings glowed in the intensity. So bright that the three travellers could no longer look. They stood, shielding themselves against the hard quartz stones, not believing. And then, the light was gone. The column of light had vanished and so had the great core of the city. The golden tendrils that had climbed so elegantly had simply ceased to be. Only the smoking wreckage of the attack that had gone before marked the city centre.

"Convinced?" Jonathan whispered.

"Let's get in." The three moved uneasily through the great outer portal, into a tunnel, and descended into the heart of the structure. "What are we hoping to find, anyway?"

They were climbing down a long stairway. Jonathan turned to her. "What do you think?" he whispered. "People, that's what."

Barnabus turned to her, his great coat flopping around his ankles. "Certainly, the inhabitants of the city must be hiding in here. We'll just have to find them."

Cathy looked up the dimly-lit passageway in front of them. "I don't know about this," she said uneasily. "Don't you think it would be better if we just waited here?"

"Waited for what? A bus?" Jonathan shook his head. "I'm going on ahead. You follow me if you want."

Barnabus and Cathy, too, moved along the passageway. The passage was proportionately as large as the rest of the monument. Its ceiling seemed to be at least fifteen metres high. The glow from its walls lit their path dimly. She mentioned this to Barnabus. He answered shortly. "Indeed. Just like Newgrange. Certainly, they have to be the same people. It would be too much of a coincidence." He looked at her. She swallowed hard, and nodded.

Jonathan called to them. The echo reverberated off the empty passage walls. They quickened their pace.

The entrance to the interior chamber was marked with a network of whorls, another reminder of its Earth ancestor. These designs far surpassed their predecessors, however. Barnabus and Cathy studied them for a moment before they moved on.

Jonathan stood in the exact centre of the chamber, next to a crystal dais which was taller than he was. He put his hands on it, looking around him. The chamber was a replica of Newgrange, but it was huge. The ceiling seemed to disappear into the shadows over their heads. Around them, the great walls were covered with quartz, waiting for the power which would give them life.

He turned to Barnabus. "Hey! At least we've found a chamber. I bet it operates just like the one at home. Now all you have to do is climb up there, punch this thing into gear, and off we go."

Barnabus walked toward the dais, a cautious look on his face. "Interesting," he said. "Yes, perhaps I can make it work. It's larger, but the principles are probably the same." Slowly, Barnabus walked around the dais. Then, he stopped, bending over for a moment. He put up a hand, motioning Jonathan and Cathy to join him. Barnabus squatted in front of an opening in the giant quartz crystal, an opening much like the one he had found in Newgrange. It was empty.

On the floor, scattered around the opening, were fragments of quartz. Barnabus picked up one of them, studying it. He handed the piece of rock to Jonathan. "It's still warm."

Jonathan took it. "So it is." He looked at the scholar sharply. "Which means?"

Barnabus rose, studying the dais. He put his hands in the pockets of his overcoat. "In my opinion," he said, "this place has been plundered. Whatever was in the quartz opening, and I have no doubt it was the focal source for the chamber's powers, has been stolen."

"Can you fix it?"

He shook his head. "Not with the supplies I have with me. Anyway, my briefcase is lying on the bottom of that stream. Or in the belly of that creature. Whatever, we've nothing to make the chamber function."

Cathy sat down on the suitcase, staring at the floor. "So we've no way home."

Barnabus shrugged. "No way that I can see. Not now, anyway." He smoothed his moustache. "If we could only find the people . . . the creators of this place. Then, perhaps . . . "

"Yes, but where are the people?"

Barnabus looked at Cathy, not saying anything.

"Look, I don't mean to be impatient," Jonathan turned to them, hands on hips. "But can't we get on with it? Let's face it, we haven't found anyone. The place is deserted. Obviously, whoever built this place have been killed, taken prisoner, or have taken the opportunity to leave."

Barnabus looked up. "Meaning, perhaps, that we should leave too."

Cathy rose, facing both of them. "Doesn't any of this unnerve you two? Here we are, heaven alone knows how many miles from home. We've witnessed some sort of incredible attack, and now we're walking through a crazy structure which looks remarkably similar to the monument at Newgrange." She hugged herself with both arms. "This place gives me the creeps. I think we should leave. It's the only sane thing for us to do."

"But where to go, Catherine. Where to go?" Barnabus stood, puzzled. Cathy sat back down on the suitcase. A feeling of impending disaster struck her. She wanted to go home . . . just to go home. She sat, looking up into the darkness of the chamber, not quite seeing, not quite caring. The quartz-lined walls of the place seemed to move up and out, disappearing into an infinity that she did not comprehend. As she watched, she didn't notice at first as the shadows moved. Small eddies washed toward her, like clouds marching before a gentle spring breeze. As she watched, the eddies became larger, drifting slowly down from the ceiling of the chamber, turning into a single dark misty shape which now grew more solid. Cathy tried to speak, but she couldn't say anything. Instead, she pointed.

The shape now stood before them, light shining from within, warm light reaching out past the vapour of the cloud, elongating, becoming more discernible. Transforming at last into a recognisable shape and that shape was a woman.

She was old, with long grey hair streaming across a gown of snow-white wool. Her body shimmered slightly, almost translucent. Cathy rose, walking away from her, back toward Barnabus and Jonathan who stood at the dais.

The old woman smiled at them. "We have been expecting you," she said, her voice sounding almost regal. "I am Kristiana. I welcome you to the New Atlantis."

19

They had not seen the stairway at the bottom of the chamber because it simply had not been there before. Now, the old woman moved quickly across the chamber floor, thrusting her arms out suddenly. For a moment, the atmosphere in the chamber rippled, a movement of light out of darkness, and a doorway yawned beneath them, a series of stairs disappearing down into the earth. "Come," she said. "Quickly. Borgnoff has been here. He may return."

She led them down a rough set of stairs which had been cut out of the rock. The walls of the stairway were split and fissured, and here and there water poured, tumbling past them, throwing up a fine mist that soaked their clothes and faces. Cathy walked close to Jonathan. He looked up at her and smiled slightly, reassuring. Halfway down the set of stairs, they were joined by a small contingent of soldiers. These men wore an armour of grey and black, seemingly made of a lightweight material, covering them completely from feet to neck. Their heads were exposed, bearded and with long dark hair. They walked warily, as if expecting to be attacked at any moment. One of them was injured, holding his right arm awkwardly, blood seeping down along his hand, dripping from his splayed fingers.

The stairs ended and they continued along through a small passageway. This came to a sudden dead end. Again, the old woman held her hands in front of her. The dim light seemed to shimmer for a moment. The rock wall disappeared, and they passed through into a small cubicle hewn directly out of the stone. From here, they could see a number of other passageways leading off in different directions.

As they entered, a group of people hurried up to them, some surrounding the wounded man, others leading the group of armoured soldiers out of the cubicle and down the passageways. A short-set man dressed in fighting armour broke away from the main group, hurrying up to the older woman.

"Kristiana, I'm glad you're back. You saw?"

She looked at him, nodding briefly. "Yes, I saw. The city is gone."

"And they have sacked the monument?"

Silently, she nodded. Cathy thought that her eyes held a great sadness. Then the old woman motioned to Cathy, Jonathan and Barnabus. "These are the three we have been expecting." She turned to them. "This is Traun. Go with him. He will make you comfortable." Barnabus started to object but Kristiana silenced him with a look. "I assure you," she said levelly, "that I will explain all. Go, now and I will visit you shortly."

The three were ushered out of the small chamber, and moved quickly down a passageway. The smaller man led the way, roughly pushing aside anybody who blocked the passage. They came to another small room. Pillows lay on the floor in a heap. Traun pointed. "These are your quarters." He gave them a glance, his black eyes darting from beneath steel grey eyebrows. "Stay here until you are summoned. Soon we will bring you new clothes and food."

He turned then, leaving them.

Cathy, exhausted, fell into the pillows. She felt a tear make its way down her cheek. Angrily, she wiped it away. She would have time to cry later. Jonathan stood, looking out the doorway, watching as people hurried along the passage. Barnabus lowered himself wearily to the ground, and sat for a moment, lost in thought.

He looked up at them suddenly. "Did I hear them correctly?"

Jonathan turned, sullen. "Which part?"

"That they were expecting us?"

Cathy nodded a little. "I heard it."

Their teacher nodded. "As I thought. They must have seen us coming."

"How?" Jonathan asked.

"Logically, if they have the same power which we discovered in Newgrange or an even greater power, then they were able to use that to detect our arrival."

Jonathan shook his head. "I don't know, Barnabus. If they have such a power, how do you account for what's happening to them?" He started to pace around the room. "Didn't you see what happened outside? The whole damn city disappeared! *Vam*! One minute it's there, the next minute it's gone. God only knows how many people were killed." He shook his head. "And did you see the state of those soldiers? It looked like they'd been through a bloody battle – and lost. I don't know, Barnabus. To me, it looks like any power they had is long gone. I mean, if they had this power, wouldn't they be able to get out of here? Transport the whole place to a new planet or something?"

Barnabus shook his head.

"One thing's for sure. They're in trouble." Cathy looked at both of them from her rough bed of pillows. "Didn't you notice that old woman? How sad she was?"

Barnabus sighed. "You're right, of course. Whatever is attacking them is doing so with great purpose."

"Do you think they'll want us to help them?" Jonathan looked down at Barnabus.

The teacher shrugged his shoulders. "Now, what could we possibly do to help them in this situation?"

Jonathan never got a chance to reply. Traun strode into the room, thrusting a bundle at them. "Clothes," he said. "Change into them quickly. Kristiana wants to see you three as soon as you're ready." He turned, leaving them.

Jonathan opened the bundle. A pile of cloth fell on the floor. "Clothes?" he said.

Cathy came over, picking out a long brown garment. "Clothes," she confirmed, smiling. "Mind you, I wouldn't say that they are the latest fashion. Better than our wet things, though."

Jonathan shook his head. "Well, when in Rome . . . Isn't that what you're always saying, Barnabus?" He shrugged off his shirt. "Maybe now we can find out what's going on."

They changed quickly, Jonathan laughing when he saw Barnabus. Their old teacher had dressed in a loose fitting costume of white wool tunic and trousers. Brown boots completed the ensemble. He would not, however, part with his treasured overcoat. His notes, now dried, had been stuffed back into the many pockets.

Cathy hid beneath a great mound of pillows and loose bedding, seeking what little privacy she could. Now, the pillows were thrown back, and Jonathan looked at the girl, who had undergone a complete transformation. She was a woman. The soft brown wool gown tumbled straight from her shoulders. Her dark hair flowed down her back. For a moment, he stared, uncertain what to say.

She coughed slightly, embarrassed. "What's the matter with you?"

He smiled awkwardly. "Nothing. You look different, that's all."

She laughed. "I look different? You should see yourself."

He flicked at the sleeve of his own white tunic, rather pleased with his new look. "I don't know if it's the latest fashion or not but it has a certain feel about it. Wonder what the kids at home would say?"

Cathy smiled. "They'd say you've gone crazy."

He smiled. "Maybe I have." They were interrupted then. Traun marched back into the room, hands on hips, surveying his charges critically. He exhaled audibly. "I guess you'll have to do. Come. We're late." They followed the older man out of the room and down the passageway.

The room which they entered held a single great table. Around it, twenty or more men and women sat, talking quietly among themselves. At the top of the table sat two people, the older woman, whom they now knew was Kristiana, and a younger man. He looked at them intently. Traun led them in, guiding the trio to the far end of the table. The small crowd grew silent, waiting.

Kristiana rose and stood before them. Cathy looked at her, appraising her. For some reason, the older woman did not look quite real. The ice-blue eyes held a vacant look; the skin, a pale white, was taut along a prominent nose. Grey hair cascaded, almost unnaturally, falling straight down her back. She was still dressed in the white gown which Cathy had seen before.

The younger man sitting next to her also looked odd. He looked at Cathy, unblinking, black eyes protruding from a smooth olive-brown face. Around them both, the air itself seemed to breathe, shimmering, almost dancing. The old woman spoke, then, and Cathy found herself looking deeply into those unfathomable blue eyes.

"I am Kristiana, leader of this city," she smiled sadly, "or should I say what is left of this city. This," she placed her hand on the shoulder of the man next to her, "is my son, Psorsis. He governs with me. We both welcome you."

She paused for a moment, thinking. "There is one thing I must ask: why have you come here?"

Barnabus cleared his throat, trying to collect his thoughts. "You might say, Kristiana," he stopped suddenly, uncertain. "I may call you Kristiana? Well, you might say that we came looking for you."

The old woman smiled at this. "Please go on."

"To explain, I must first ask you a question, if you don't mind?" Kristiana nodded. Barnabus scratched his head, then smoothed his moustache in thought. "Did you, by any chance, have anything to do with the construction of a rather unique mound? A mound located on what I can only refer to as Earth, the third planet in a system of nine planets." He studied her quizzically, as though he were testing one of his maths students. "To be more precise, the mound in which we're standing happens to look very much like one not far from where we live, though it is much smaller. I should also state that the structure has some very unusual characteristics: it taps local energy fields including magnetic, water and heat sources, utilising these to produce some rather . . . ahhh . . . unique behaviour."

Kristiana nodded. "Our initial attempt. Yes, our people constructed that many, many years ago."

Barnabus clapped his hands together, in triumph. "I knew it. I knew that I would find you!"

Jonathan looked to the ceiling. "Barnabus," he said in warning. "We're not in class. Calm down!"

Kristiana studied him intently. "So you have come merely to find the creators of the mound?"

Barnabus almost giggled with excitement. "Of course! Once I began to understand the workings of the structure, once I began to see how to control it, I became anxious to find the people that had created it. You did, of course, leave your little road map. It was a great help, that."

Kristiana arched her eyebrows. "Road map?"

Barnabus mumbled quickly. "Yes, sorry. The symbol of the mound. The great whorl. It showed us where you might be found. It led us to this system. It took us a while, but find you we did!"

Kristiana regarded him intently. "But the mound was inactive when we left it. The focal point of power had been taken."

Barnabus looked at her in excitement. "You mean the quartz dais? Yes, I noticed that it lacked its core. I guessed, and it turned out rightly, that the interior had contained a mechanism to focus the power, enabling the operator to bend that power to his will. Or hers, for that matter," he added, deferentially.

The old woman was puzzled. "But how could you?"

Barnabus blushed with the embarrassment of the inventor. "Actually, it was quite easy. The mathematics involved were simple enough, once I had an understanding of the power sources. Putting together the actual mechanism was straight forward. A few bits of old electronics. Some microchips. Nothing to it, really."

Kristiana nodded, for a moment thinking. "We have watched Earth, as you call it, develop for thousands of years. Ever since we fled from it. I had no idea that its people had grown so knowledgeable. And who, may I ask, operated the power source?"

Barnabus coloured a little. "Well, actually, I did."

Kristiana laughed in amusement. "So, you have used it to follow its original makers. I congratulate you." She grew serious. "It is a pity that you have come at this time in our history. What you have witnessed is only the beginning of a great battle. It is a battle between an intelligence which is far greater even than our own." Her impassive face saddened. "In this battle, we have been the victims. We do not understand yet the magnitude of the power which we face. We only know that so far, we have been unable to stop the destruction which they have wrought."

Barnabus looked at the old woman, puzzled. "But surely, with the power which you can harness, you are able to defend yourselves?"

Kristiana stood rigid. "No," she said. "They have robbed us of that power. They have stolen the single element that would enable us to defend our civilisation. They have stolen the scrolls of Psorsis."

Barnabus shook his head, not understanding. Kristiana lowered her head in resignation. "We knew that you were coming, but we were powerless to stop you." She glanced at them. "Perhaps, however, it is well that you did come. You might help us." She thought for a moment. "You will eat first. Then, with my son, I will tell you our story. Perhaps then, we shall see what we might do together."

20

They ate quickly and then Traun took them back to their rooms. "You will wait here," he said. "When they want you, they will ask for you." He left.

Cathy spoke first. "Did you take a good look at Kristiana, Barnabus? And her son? They looked almost like mannequins."

Jonathan agreed. "I noticed that, too. As if they weren't alive at all. And did you see the air around them? It shimmered like water."

"Or like a power source, which I suggest it might have been." He thought for a moment. "What I can't understand is what they meant when stating that they had been robbed of their power. Unless . . . " His hands moved to his moustache, stroking it in thought. "Do you remember when we first entered the large chamber?"

"You mean the one in Newgrange?"

"No, no," he replied impatiently. "Here. Above us. You remember that the dais had been broken into. That the focal point of its power had been stolen."

"Sure, I remember." Jonathan nodded. "But certainly they can replace that. I mean if you did it, Barnabus, certainly they can." He looked at the teacher. "Hey, I didn't mean it to sound that way."

"No, no. Quite right you are. Certainly, they would have the tools to make the dais function again. Unless . . . " Barnabus thought for a moment. "Unless, for some reason, they have never had to develop those tools."

"You are, of course, quite correct." The voice came without substance, without direction. Barnabus stood still, shocked. "Kristiana?" he asked timidly. The faces of Kristiana and Psorsis emerged from the wall of their chamber, hanging suspended above them, disembodied. The faces were expressionless, passive. The eyes staring into space. Only the mouths moved when they talked.

"Your intelligence is obvious. I am proud of it. When I left your planet, I thought then that any survivors would sink back into raceless extinction. I was wrong, and glad of it."

Barnabus cocked his head. "You said that you left the Earth, Kristiana? But that's not possible. Newgrange has been disused for thousands of years."

The leader of the Atlanteans smiled a little. "Yes. My son and I and a thousand others of our kind. We left your Earth – our Earth – more than five thousand of your years ago."

"But that's impossible!"

"Nothing is impossible, Barnabus. You know that. During the transport to this new planet, Psorsis and I experienced the power of the mound longer than any of our fellow citizens. It altered the composition of our bodies. In many ways, we have become part of the energy which is in all things. We are still mortal, of course. We can die. But our bodies have been altered. We have lived for thousands of years. It is a great gift. But we gave up much more. In many ways, we have given up our humanity. Even the others whom you have met here, they are no longer what they once were. Granted, they have kept their physical properties intact. But their offspring no longer carry the natural powers which our people once had. That has been lost. Our genes have been altered irrevocably. It means that we no longer are what we once were." She sighed. "It is my greatest wish that we recover our humanity. To that end, we have been studying Earth intently, waiting for the day when we might again rejoin you. We hoped that we would again recapture the heritage of humanity which was once ours. Now, however, even survival is jeopardised." Her image stirred. "Perhaps your coming is a message of new hope."

For a moment, the hovering figures faded, seeming to lose their shape. Slowly, they regained their structure. Kristiana spoke again. "The power of this planet has been interrupted yet again. Shortly, the intelligence which is attacking us will start upon its final assault. I must tell you our story, and there is not much time. First, you must know that we are related, however distantly. Your genes hold the keys to our lost heritage. And that heritage is the people and culture which is the lost civilisation of Atlantis."

Barnabus fell into the bedding of their room, his mouth open. "You talk of Atlantis? Atlantis? But, Atlantis is only a legend."

The figure next to Kristiana shook his head. "No. It was real – and our people are part of that reality. Listen, now, and we shall tell you all."

The story did not take much time. Quickly, Kristiana and Psorsis told them of the destruction of the continent of Atlantis. Of the comet Borgnoff – the Destroyer – which deliberately destroyed the great civilisation which held so much hope for the world.

She told them of her grandfather, Psorsis, of the secrets which he had discovered, of the scrolls which he had written to safeguard those secrets. She talked of the journey of Midreas as he set out to save the scrolls, and of the monument that he had created, even then knowing that the natural powers underneath the earth could be harnessed once the secrets of the scrolls had been unlocked. She then spoke of the part that she had played in unlocking the secrets that Psorsis had bequeathed her. She recounted the empowerment of the monument and the ways she and her son had used that power to further their understanding of the universe.

Finally, she told of the malevolent intelligence that had returned to Earth and of the great attack; of the barrier of energy which they had erected to defend their planet; and of the final evacuation which had brought them to this new planet. She mentioned the few that had remained on Earth, and how she had wept for them, thinking that they would be destroyed in the final barrage of power. "These, and our few survivors, these were your ancestors. Through you, their blood, and ours, still flows."

For a moment, she stopped, then said with great passion: "For five thousand years, the survivors of Atlantis have toiled on this planet to re-establish the Atlantean heritage of peace, knowledge and understanding. And, over those years, we have succeeded. What you have seen is a civilisation greater than any known on Earth. From having nothing, we learned from the scrolls to harness the power of this planet and with it to build great cities. To harvest the foods from the waters and the soil. To come to a greater knowledge of ourselves and to work with our fellow citizens to understand the universe around us.

"We have travelled great distances, using that power. We have explored many parts of the universe which had lain unknown. But always, we returned here. We are a peaceful people. Our last endeavour was to return to the womb of our people and by so doing, to recapture the humanity which we had lost so long ago. By mixing the blood of our ancestors with the blood of our new civilisation, we believed that we would become a people of even greater intelligence – a people capable of surviving until the end of time.

"This is what my grandfather Psorsis wanted for us. It was his greatest wish that the culture of Atlantis be saved from extinction. Now, after so many years, that wish might finally die."

Her voice grew angry. "For thousands of years, a blackness has covered the face of this universe, moving from system to system, searching for conscious life which might, for whatever reason, threaten its claim to rule. This putrid intelligence – we call it Borgnoff – destroyed the original continent of Atlantis, killing Psorsis in the process. It forced us from the very surface of our planet, making us flee across the trackless wastes of space. Now, it has found us again. This time, this third time, it seems it intends to finish that destruction."

Jonathan, listening, had also grown angry. "That's not right.

You have done nothing to make them attack. Certainly, you can defend yourselves."

The shimmering face smiled sadly. "It is as your teacher has said. We are powerless. It was so simple that we did not see the flaw. The scrolls themselves are the key to our power. The knowledge which they contain has provided us with incredible understanding. But they held more than that for us. Each page of the scrolls was housed in a special material made by Psorsis himself. These held physical properties which we have never been able to replicate. The scrolls were an access to all natural power. They were capable of focusing energies, directing them. Harnessed by an intelligent mind, their uses are unimaginable. Even after so many years, we have still not realised all their potential."

Barnabus had been listening intently, but now he raised his head. "And this is where you think we can help?"

"Yes. For whatever reason, our cultures have taken different paths. We have always worked best with our minds, using the natural elements which we have found around us, moulding these simple entities to our use. Your culture, on the other hand, has devised other methods. Your understanding of complex structures is much greater than ours. For instance, I am amazed that you were able to construct a substitute for the scrolls. Yet, you did. Somehow, you managed to focus the energy outputs beneath the monument without the need for the scrolls. It is, after all, how you got here."

"And now, you're hoping that I can again create a substitute for the scrolls."

"Yes." She stated it simply, with hope.

Barnabus rose and faced her. Sadly, he shook his head. "What you ask is impossible, Kristiana. I have lost most of my tools. Those that I do have are almost worthless. Even then, the power of this monument must be vast. Huge. I don't know that I could harness it for your aims."

"But you could try?"

Barnabus looked up at the old leader's distraught face. He cleared his throat. "And if I could create such a tool for you,

you would then be able to defend yourselves?"

Psorsis spoke. "With the power of this planet at our disposal we can ward off any attack. We cannot defeat the intelligence itself, but we can defend ourselves from total conquest."

Barnabus stood, thinking. "I will try. God knows that I don't have much with me. But I can at least try." He thought for a moment longer, then looked up at them. "In case I fail, do you have any other plan?"

Psorsis spoke again. "Borgnoff has stolen the scrolls of Psorsis from us. He understands their power, their knowledge. With those at his disposal, he would become unstoppable." His face shimmered. "We are formulating a plan to get them back. We shall steal them from under the very nose of Borgnoff."

"With the scrolls again in our possession, we will have a source of power which, I believe, is many times greater than the darkness which we fight." The pale figure of Kristiana moved toward them. "This is our hope. We will be able to rid the universe once and for all of the evil that tried to destroy our culture in the time of my grandfather and which plagues us to this day."

Barnabus put his hands firmly into his pockets, considering. He looked up at the glimmering figures. "Well then, if you would be so kind as to have my bags brought down, I will get started. We both have a great deal of work to do. I suppose I'd best be getting down to it, hadn't I?"

The network of underground passageways became a hive of activity. Groups of people rushed here and there, moving to carry out some order that they had been given. Every now and then, the underground caverns shook slightly. The bombardment was continuing above them. Cathy and Jonathan stood at the door to their room, watching the excitement. Barnabus took his two students aside. "We may not be in class," he said, "but I expect you to follow a few simple directions.

"First, stay out of the way of these people . . . ah, these Atlanteans." He sighed a little. "I suppose I'd best get used to calling them by their right names, as fantastic as it seems. They have a great deal to do and I doubt that they need you two running around under their skirts. Secondly, you can give me a hand." He turned to Jonathan. "They brought down the cases?"

"Yes." Jonathan nodded to the corner of their room where the computer and suitcase sat. "I hope the effort of hauling those here was worth it."

Barnabus walked over to the pile, picking up his battered suitcase. "If this works, your efforts will have been worth it. If not . . . " His face was grave. "If not, I'd hate to think of the outcome."

He unlocked the case, spilling the contents out on the floor. A small stream of water followed, a souvenir of their time in the wet gully. Spare electronic parts lay in the middle of a tangle of clothes. He looked at them, uncertain. "God only knows what shape they're in. We'll just have to have some faith in the manufacturer." He picked up a microprocessor. "Most of my materials are in the briefcase. And that's untouchable." He sighed. "I'll just have to make do."

Absently, he patted his coat, looking into his pockets. "Let's see," he muttered as he looked. "No, that's not it. Sidereal coordinates. No. Ah, calculations on energy fields, no. Ahhh!" He looked up. "Mrs O'Neill's recipe for soda bread. I've been looking for that." He shrugged sheepishly, going back to the pockets. "Archeological digs at the pyramids, last summer's exam paper . . . ah, here!" He pulled a wad of paper from an inside pocket. "This is it." He separated the pages, spreading them, one after another, on the floor. Jonathan and Cathy looked down on a series of highly complex calculations. On the final two pages was a pencilled sketch. Jonathan could just make out four separate panels. They were electronic diagrams.

"This," their teacher spoke almost reverently, patting the diagrams gently, "this is the modus. The method. The way!" He paused, mesmerised, almost in a dream.

Jonathan and Cathy looked at each other and back at their teacher. "The way to what, Barnabus?"

He snapped back from wherever he had been. "Sorry. It is, of course, my greatest triumph. These," he touched the series of equations, "are the mathematics which gave me the first glimmer – the first inkling of the powers which lay under Newgrange. As I worked through them, I began to understand the thinking of those earlier peoples, to guess at the powers which they tamed and the manner in which they tamed them." He put his hands in his coat pockets reflectively. "I could not believe that they had the ability to control the forces of nature. But I knew that the chamber which I found had to be used for something. At first, I thought it was a tomb or a place for religious ceremonies. Well, why not? The quartz dais resembles an altar, does it not?" The students nodded in agreement. "But I felt something. Something which I can't explain. Deep inside me." He glanced at them, almost embarrassed. "As a scholar, I do not usually deal in feelings. Yet, there they were. That's when I began my study of the actual monument." He began to pace around the little room. "I realised that the siting of the monument was no accident. I studied it intently. I conducted my own surveys of the location. The magnetic variations which surround Newgrange indicated a great potential source of power. Enough even to bend the forces of gravity.

"Late one night it came to me. I understood, then. Newgrange was a great tool, used by the ancients – or should I say the Atlanteans – for some unknown purpose. I reexamined the structure, visiting the chamber many times over the weeks. I even built the model which you saw, in an attempt to give me additional clues as to its use. Then I had another look at the dais. And that's when I discovered the cavity that the ancients placed there. Something was contained in that cavity, but what?"

He paused, remembering. "I dreamed about it, so plagued was I by that problem. I knew that by solving that riddle, I would solve the riddle of the monument itself. I spent hours thinking of how it could be used, of what it had contained. But I got nowhere. At one point, I contemplated abandoning the entire venture. Then, a strange thing happened."

"Which was?" Cathy prodded.

"I was in the chamber, standing on the dais itself. Suddenly, I had what could best be described as a vision. I saw the chamber as it was. The power in the great belly of the earth surged upwards, into the dais. It glowed bright, focusing that power, transmitting it upward into those who stood on the dais, enabling them to bend that power to their will.

"The vision ended. I knew then that the dais was the storer of the great powers which surrounded it. Whatever had been contained in the dais was used to focus those powers. To transform its raw energy, harnessing it into a source of power which no man – not even the most clever nuclear physicist – had yet devised.

"It was simple, then. The mathematics came as if I knew them already. And the diagram came, too. Simplicity itself. Some spare parts, a couple of microprocessing units, and *voilà*! The thing was done."

Jonathan stirred slightly. He had been listening intently to Barnabus, and now he began to understand the significance of what his teacher said. "So you've discovered how to control natural energy. Which means that men now have an unlimited source of power at their disposal."

His teacher smiled. "Remember, Jonathan, I didn't discover it. The Atlanteans discovered it. I've merely uncovered that which they have already found. As to controlling natural power . . . " He was silent, considering. "I suspect that my simple electronic mechanism is child's play compared with the brilliance of the original scrolls. I do hope that they're able to recover them! I shall do my best to build a working replica of my simple apparatus . . . " He glanced at the small pile of electronic equipment. " . . . if, of course, I have the parts for it. And, I can only hope that it will handle the power output which this vast complex – this greater Newgrange – probably generates." He looked at them, soberly. "Let us hope that their venture succeeds, and that they recover the lost scrolls. I would hate to think that my insignificant capabilities will be tested to their limits."

The cavern shook again. Barnabus fell to his knees from the impact. He looked up at the ceiling. Cracks appeared in the great carved rocks. "Whatever our options, I suggest that we hurry."

21

"Come on. The meeting room is only a little further down this passageway."

"You heard what Barnabus said. He told us to stay in the room."

Jonathan looked over his shoulder at Cathy as they slipped quietly along the passage. "What does he care if we look around a little? Anyway, from the sound of the battle overhead, we don't have much time. If we're going to die in this crummy place, I'd just as soon know what's going on."

They were now jogging down a passageway, trying to find their way through the maze of tunnels which honeycombed the ground underneath the monument. Atlanteans passed with scarcely a second glance at them. They had left Barnabus sitting in his small pile of electronic gear – circuit boards, wire, microprocessors, diodes. He tested his battery-operated soldering iron. "Still works, thank God," he stated in a relieved voice. "I must send a testimonial to the manufacturer."

They asked him if they could be any help but he was already wrapped up in his notes. "Hmm? No, no, that's not necessary. Run along and give a man time to work." They left him, then, deciding to see if they could find Kristiana.

"She'll be busy, Jonathan," Cathy said to him, ice in her voice.

"Sure she'll be busy. But I'm not going to sit around with nothing to do. Come on; we have to do something to save our hides."

Cathy stopped walking. "But what about the mechanism that Barnabus is working on? For God's sake, Jonathan, surely he'll be able to fix us up."

He smirked. "He got us into this mess in the first place. You can't possibly think that his bag full of spare parts is going to give us a solution, can you?" He waited for her to answer but she didn't say anything. "I don't know about you, but I want to get home alive. And the only way home seems to be through those damn scrolls that Kristiana keeps talking about. Now if it's all right with you, I'm going to see if I can lend a hand."

"Can we just be careful for a change?"

"You be careful. I'm going to find those scrolls. Come on if you're coming." He started up the passage. Cathy stood for a second, then followed.

At the end of the passage was a large door framed in the symbolic whorls of Newgrange. Jonathan and Cathy stopped, pressing themselves against the passage wall. Slowly, Jonathan eased his way up to the opening, peering around the corner of the door.

In a large room, a contingent of twenty fighting men stood to attention, each dressed in the black armour that they had seen before. At their head, standing tall and proud, was Kristiana. At her side was Psorsis. Kristiana looked towards the door, as if sensing their presence. She spoke directly to Jonathan and Cathy. "You may come in. Perhaps you will have some advice to give."

They entered quietly. Cathy gave Jonathan a sharp look as she whispered, "Do me a favour, will you, Jonathan? For a change, don't say anything, OK?"

Kristiana gestured for them to come closer. "Stand over here, next to Traun. You have already met, I believe?" They nodded. "Traun is commandant of our fighting troops. He is the direct descendant of my father, a great warrior called Rengal. He has planned the attack which will retake the scrolls from Borgnoff."

Traun said quietly, "I simply wish, Kristiana, that you would let me go with the others."

The old woman smiled, shaking her head. "You know that is not possible. Psorsis will go. It is his right to bring back the scrolls, and I cannot let both of you face possible destruction. No, my friend," she placed her hand gently on the fighting man's shoulder, "your task is to stay here, to guard the remnants of our people."

Jonathan spoke up. "You mean you're not going to wait until Barnabus is finished?"

Kristiana shook her head slightly. "No. Since he cannot be sure that he can help us we have decided to recapture the scrolls ourselves."

"Then I want to go too."

Cathy put her hand on top of Jonathan's, squeezing it. "Jonathan! Will you shut up?"

"No way. If he's going . . . " Jonathan pointed at Psorsis " . . . then I'm going."

Psorsis smiled at him a little coldly. "That won't be necessary. I doubt that you would be able to contribute to our effort."

"What do you mean by that! I'm not going to just sit here while this Borgnoff creature tries to burn us alive."

"No, he is right. You have no training, Jonathan." Kristiana looked at him, not unkindly. "It is better you stay here. You may be of assistance to your scholar. And I'm certain that Cathy would miss you."

Cathy looked down, seeing her hand still on Jonathan's. Quickly, she withdrew it, her cheeks burning. Kristiana looked at her. "No, Jonathan. It is my order that you stay here. And you shall obey."

"Well if that's the way you want it!" Jonathan strode to the door. "I'll be with Barnabus."

Kristiana followed him with her eyes. "He still has the fire of youth in his belly. Perhaps, it shall prove to be of use." She turned, then, looking at Cathy. "You should join him, I think. See that he stays out of trouble." Kristiana smiled at her. "It is the fate of women always to protect their men."

Cathy blushed. "Yes. I'll go to him." She left the table,

following Jonathan out the door.

Kristiana watched them go. Then she took up a great shimmering globe which had been lying on the table. It was a globe of purest glass crystal. In its exact centre, a point of pure white light glimmered, as small and as unobtrusive as starlight. She stood, composed in thought, her face a mask of concentration. Purposefully, she raised her arm, as if in blessing.

The light in the centre of the globe intensified, growing brighter, almost blinding in its intensity. Bolts of light danced from it, touching everything in the room. It played over the twenty fighting men. Their armour began to glimmer, seeming to radiate a growing energy. They stood, twenty brightly lit sentinels, bright white ghosts, shining with armour that was at once clear and opaque. When she had finished, Kristiana placed the globe again on the table.

"Now you have such protection as I can give you. It is not much. It cannot totally guard you against the power of Borgnoff, for its power is greater than mine!" She looked at them, eyes blazing. "You are our last hope. If you can reach the scrolls in time, then all is not lost. With them, I can defend us against the wrath of Borgnoff. Without them . . . " Her voice trailed off. "Atlantis may well have met its end."

Jonathan stepped back from the door, to where Cathy was waiting. They had hidden behind the rock of the doorway, watching Kristiana energise her people. Jonathan turned, wiping the perspiration from his forehead. "I don't know about you, but it's going to take a while for me to get used to these people."

"What happened?"

He smiled wickedly. "Not much. Just that Kristiana surrounded them with some sort of energy field. It's supposed to protect them. God knows, though, if I had to go up against those lightning bolts blasting from the heavens, I'd want more than a little energy field protecting me."

Cathy nodded. "So, now what do you intend to do?"

Jonathan smiled a little. "I've got a plan."

"I was afraid of that. Look, you heard Kristiana. She told you to stay put."

"No way. I am *not* staying here." He took her by the shoulders. "Kristiana thinks that the scrolls are our only way out. I have no intention of meeting my end in this place. And . . . " he looked at her, "I'd just as soon see you safe back home."

"Fine, Jonathan. It's great to know you care. But I'm not letting you disobey Kristiana."

The sound of movement came from the inner chamber. "Quick. Over here." They darted across the entrance, hiding behind a column of rough rock. From the doorway, the small militia emerged, Psorsis at their head. They moved silently down the passage. Jonathan waited a second, took a deep breath and followed.

"Are you crazy?" Cathy hissed. "Where do you think you're going?"

He turned around. "Be quiet!" he whispered.

"You're not going with them, are you?"

"Sure. I told you." He touched her briefly on the shoulder. "Got to keep in with the action. You go back and tell Barnabus. I'll be all right." He turned, moving up the passageway after the troopers.

Cathy stood for a moment, undecided. Then she followed Jonathan.

The city was a mass of rubble. Smoke curled into the cloud-covered sky, tinted purple from the great red sun which circled this strange world. Puddles of gold lay cooling on the ground, bright lakes amid the torn and beaten remnants of what had been a magnificent city.

Jonathan ran, hiding behind walls of pure gold, keeping up with the raiding party, trying not to lose them. The attack had lessened. Now, only an occasional flicker of light stabbed from clouds to ground, mopping up anything which was not already wasted. He couldn't believe it. The power which these creatures controlled must be vast! In a few hours, they had destroyed what must have taken hundreds of years to construct.

He looked at the troops walking ahead of him. "And they think that they're just going to walk in under Borgnoff's nose and take back the scrolls," he muttered. "They must have some screws loose, despite their brainpower."

The troops stopped. Jonathan scurried to the shell of a building, hiding in the rubble. Carefully, he edged round a corner, trying to keep his eyes on the troops.

"And just what do you think you're doing?"

Jonathan dropped to his belly, striking his head on the wall. He grabbed his forehead, rolling over to see Cathy standing behind him. "Dammit, Cathy. You could have warned me that you were there."

"I did." She smiled. "Your reaction times are pretty good, all things considered. Too bad you haven't figured out how to stop banging yourself up."

"Ha ha." He rubbed his head for a second. "What are you doing here, anyway?"

"I thought I should come along. Try to keep you out of trouble."

"Great," he muttered.

She crossed her arms. "Well, if you don't want me here, I'll leave."

"Good. I don't want you here. I told you to stay with Barnabus."

"What am I? Your dog?"

He looked up at her. "You making comparisons?"

"You haven't done so well. You almost got us killed. Remember?"

"All right, all right. Just stay out of the way." Jonathan got back up on his hands and knees, trying to edge around the corner of the building.

"What are you doing?"

"Well, if you want to know, the troops, or whatever the hell they are, are standing right over there." He pointed.

She came up behind him, leaning on his shoulder. "Over there?"

"Hey, get off me, will you? Yeah, if you're interested at all."

"Where are they going?"

"How should I know?" He looked again. "Come on. They're moving." He glanced at her. "Just keep low, will you? I don't want them to see us." Jonathan moved out of the hiding place. He moved along the wall, keeping flat against it. Cathy followed.

The troops were walking away from the city. They crossed a tract of grassland, keeping low. Jonathan watched as they entered a forest of tall tree-like vegetation. He followed, Cathy behind him. They rested for a minute, leaning against one of the trees. "You sure they went in here?"

"Yes, I'm sure." He turned. "Why, don't you want to follow them?"

Cathy looked into the gloom of the forest. "It looks dark."

"Of course it's dark. It's a forest. Come on." They started walking.

It was quiet. All they could hear was the sound of their own footsteps as they trudged through the undergrowth. The floor of the forest was covered with moss and fallen branches. They worked hard, Jonathan leading, beating down a path for Cathy to follow. "Stop making so much noise. They'll hear us."

"How else do you think I'm going to get through this stuff? Fly over it?" Now, they entered a boggy area. Water seeped through the spongy, green matter forming a film of grey filth. The going became tougher, they sank in up to their ankles with each step. "You can sure pick trails," Cathy said.

"You want to do it?"

"No. You go right ahead."

A high-pitched whine echoed through the forest, reverberating through the dense foliage above them. "What was that?"

Jonathan stopped. "How should I know? You think I was trained in interplanetary zoology?"

Cathy shivered. "Well I didn't like it."

"Neither did I." He wiped his forehead. "I just hope that whatever it is it isn't hungry."

"Thanks a lot."

"Come on. We'd better keep up."

"You sure they went this way?"

"Yes." He pointed at the ground. "See the footprints in that muck over there?" She looked, nodding. "Come on. Let's keep going."

They walked on for over an hour. The ground became steadily worse. Now, they were skirting small ponds; giant bubbles of gas burst through a surface of green and gold slime. A smell of rotting eggs clawed at their throats, making their eyes water.

"Smells like sulphur."

Cathy held her hands over her face. "Whatever it is, I don't like it."

"Neither do I, if it makes any difference to you."

"God, it can't be much further, can it?"

Jonathan exhaled. "I don't know. These guys certainly know how to walk." He walked back to her through the muck. "You getting tired?"

She smiled a little. "Kind of."

He nodded. "I'll give you a hand." He pulled her arm around his waist; his other arm went around her waist. "Now, let's see if we can speed things up."

When they talked about it later, they recalled that they couldn't remember really hearing anything at first. Instead, they sort of felt it. The air around them seemed to vibrate a little, humming. The hair went up on Jonathan's arms. "What's that?" he whispered.

"I don't . . . "

The thing stopped just in front of them, staring. It had wings. Jonathan thought that he could count eight of them, moving so quickly along its great armoured back that they were only a blur. The single huge red eye, filled with hundreds of individual cells, gyrated back and forth, gauging what was in its path. The mandibles below the great eye slowly opened and closed, in constant motion. Its last meal, some sort of furry creature, lay half in and half out of the cavernous mouth, leaking its life's fluid on to the slimy ground. The thing in front of them looked for less than five seconds. Then it was gone, the faint vibration still surrounding them.

Jonathan looked at Cathy. "Did you see that?"

She stood glued in the muck, her mouth open slightly.

"I asked you if you saw that."

"Huh? Yes, I saw it."

Jonathan looked behind him. "Did you see where it went?"

"No."

"I don't know about you, but I want to get out of this forest."

They felt the vibration again. They stood stock still. "Do you see it?" Cathy whispered.

Jonathan shook his head. They looked around them. Slowly. "You stay here. I'm going to that tree over there. See if I can see the thing."

She nodded. The vibration grew stronger. "Hurry, will you?"

"Don't rush me. I got to get through this junk." Jonathan was wading through a small stream.

"Hey Jonathan, that vibration is getting louder."

"For God's sake, Cathy, I'm going as fast as I can." He turned around to face her. "You want to try this . . . " He looked at her. "Cathy," he said it quietly. "Whatever you do, don't move."

"What?"

"I said don't move!" Jonathan crept back to her slowly. He put out is hand to her. "Now, when I count three, we're going to run like hell."

"Jonathan, stop playing games."

"This is no game." He motioned with his head over her right shoulder. "And I don't think that thing is interested in playing either."

Slowly, she turned her head – and froze. It hovered within inches of her ear, the great green mandibles dripping flesh and blood, the gigantic eye staring into hers, its huge armoured body, at least five feet long, supported on the whirring wings. Tentatively, one of the mandibles moved toward her, telescoping out, touching her gently on the cheek.

She screamed, and started running, ignoring everything: the waterlogged ground, the small streams, the filth and slime of it all.

"Cathy! Cathy, wait!" He ran after her. "You scared the thing away."

There was no stopping her. She ran as fast as she could, crying, shaking, thinking of nothing but getting as far away as she could from the thing that had touched her. She ran until she couldn't run any more. Exhausted, she stood, shaking uncontrollably.

"I'm all right," she said, hugging herself, cold at the thought of what she had seen. She was dripping wet, the rough clothes she wore were saturated, her boots waterlogged. She turned, then, realising that she was alone. "Jonathan!" she screamed. "Jonathan! Where are you?"

Borgnoff had seen her running, splashing through the muck. Now It moved directly above Cathy, gauging her direction and speed. She was coming towards Borgnoff and for a moment It considered her a threat. In that split second, Its composite mind considered destroying her. It would be so simple. The energy which the mind controlled was vast – as great as the combined energy of the planetary system which It now dominated. It considered the option for a moment but then the other elements that were part of Its great mind argued a different course of action. The decision took only moments. Instead, the energy was re-routed; thoughts transferred at the speed of light, shaping the forces to Its will. Borgnoff could use this catch, perhaps. If not, it would be a simple matter to eliminate Cathy. Its will focused at last, the intelligence opened Its great mind, and the energy sped through the thick atmosphere, targeting directly on the exhausted creature below.

Jonathan watched and collapsed into a small pool of water, hiding just below the surface. He raised himself slightly. His eyes peered over the muck. For a second, he thought that he had gone crazy. The trees had parted, pushed aside by the energy. He looked into a vortex, a whirling pattern of light, moving down, appendages of pure energy oscillating around the vortex like cilia on a single-celled creature. Cathy was directly below it. Crying. Calling his name. He yelled to her, but too late. She looked up. Borgnoff saw her, and she screamed. The beam of pure light, intense, hot, engulfed her. Jonathan could only watch. She froze, the screaming stopped. Her body shook, buffeted in the current of energy. Dissolving. Then moving. Her outline, as faint as pure glass, rose upwards, caught up in the energy of the vortex. Caught by the moving cilia of energy, brought up and into its centre. She was gone. He watched as it moved. Up, out of the trees, rising away from him, and into the cloud cover.

22

They found him wandering through the forest, soaking, feverish, calling her name over and over again. Psorsis stood over him as his team gave the boy medical attention. The soldier, acting as a field doctor, applied a sensor roughly to the scratches and bruises which covered Jonathan's body. Psorsis looked at him, his heavy eyebrows arching behind the protective shielding which flickered in the sunlight.

The doctor shrugged. "Nothing wrong with him that I can see. Shock, mostly. Superficial cuts. Some bruises. Overexposure. Nothing that rest won't cure."

Psorsis considered. Jonathan lay on a blanket of dead leaves. A cloak of wool had been thrown over him. Sweat glistened on his face and he continued to shake uncontrollably. "Has he said anything?"

"Not much. Keeps going on about someone named Cathy."

"That's his friend. Obviously, she was with him. Has he said where she is?"

The medic looked uncomfortable. He glanced towards his leader and swallowed. "He muttered something about her disappearing."

Psorsis nodded, understanding. "So we've made contact. It will not be far now. Come. We haven't much time." He turned to go.

The soldier stood for a minute. "What about the boy?"

Psorsis turned, looking at Jonathan, shaking violently on the soggy ground, obviously unconscious. "Leave him." He walked away.

"With no weapons? No rations?"

Psorsis stopped, not looking back. "He will be safe enough here. As I said, leave him." He motioned to his troops. They followed. The doctor stood for a moment, undecided. Quickly, he bent to the ground, placing some materials beside his patient. Then he withdrew, moving to catch up with his leader.

Sunlight played brightly into Jonathan's eyes. He moved a little, groaning. His eyes flickered open, focusing on the canopy of vegetation above him. For a minute, he thought that he was home. Where am I? The sunlight was bright, warm. He stretched a little, enjoying the heat. Then he came to with a start. The rays of two globes of sun filtered through the rust-coloured trees. He looked around, remembering. The Red Giant must have set, he thought. Only two of the system's suns were visible overhead. He shook his head slightly. "Great. This is just great." He rolled over then, crawling along though the undergrowth. He stopped. His stomach rumbled. "And on top of everything, I'm hungry." He looked around, trying to clear his head. Something else was wrong. What was it?

"Cathy," he said. He got to his feet, the blanket falling to his ankles. He studied the ground intently. It was covered with footprints. He understood suddenly and started shaking again, this time with anger. "They left me!" he yelled, his voice absorbed at once by the soft ground and foliage. He stood for a moment, uncertain of what to do. Then, deciding, he picked up the blanket. He noticed the containers next. One was larger than the other, both made of a glittering gold, the whorl emblem deeply embossed on them. Dropping the blanket, he picked up the larger one, studying it intently. There were no obvious latches. He touched the emblem on the larger container. At once, the outside facing disappeared, revealing an array of green packets, all the same size. He selected one, holding it in the palm of his hand. At once, the packet began to vibrate slightly. He tried to drop it, but the packet stuck firmly to his hand. He watched. The packet ceased vibrating. Instead it began to change colour. From green, to blue, to red, working its way through the spectrum. Warmth spread into his hand, up his arm. Finally, the packet glowed a bright red, then seemed to cool, running back through the colour spectrum and changing finally to black. He turned his hand over and the packet fell to the ground. He raised his head, feeling better, somehow. He realised, then. The packet had somehow nourished him. When he woke, Jonathan had felt hungry and thirsty. Now, while he did not feel full, he was no longer bothered by basic needs. He looked at the larger container, still held firmly in his other hand. It had sealed itself. He smiled. "An Atlantean survival kit," he said. "Now all I need is a Swiss army knife, and I'd be set."

He glanced at the other gold container lying in the muck. Carefully, he picked it up. This container was smaller, the size of a Zippo lighter, and fitted neatly into the palm of his hand. The Atlantean whorl rested just below his thumb. Tentatively, not knowing what to expect, he pressed it.

The change was immediate. One minute, he stood in his soggy clothing. The next, his body was encased in a solid suit. He held one arm up. It was housed in the protective armour which the Atlantean troops wore. He glanced down. The rest of his body was similarly protected. His head seemed to be completely free, but something had changed. His vision had been affected. At first, he thought he was seeing things. Everywhere that he looked, a faint gold whorl danced in front of him. Then he realised that the whorl was a part of his vision. Yet, when he looked at his arm – or any other part of his body – the whorl disappeared. He studied his new clothing intently. The armour covered him in a smooth, jointless case, yet was much thinner than he would have thought, and, he believed, infinitely stronger. Then he noticed. In the palms of both hands, the gold whorls danced, seemingly engraved directly into his skin. Carefully, he touched his palm with his thumb.

The concentration of energy was so startling that he jumped

back a full metre. The hole in the wool blanket which rested at his feet still smoked. He nodded, understanding a little. He decided to test his theory. This time, he was in no hurry. He looked around, finally directing the whorl which danced in front of his eyes towards the red trunk of a tree. He clenched his hand into a fist, his thumb inward. This time, he saw it. The energy at first seemed to move into him from all directions. As if he were borrowing the power available from the world around him – which, he thought, he probably was. It focused on a point a foot in front of his face, glowed intensely, then moved as a finger of light in the direction of the tree.

He walked over to the tree. It was at least two metres in diameter; yet the hole had been drilled precisely through it. Smoke curled up from the reddish wood. He grinned, sheepishly. "Well," he said to the forest around him. "I guess I found my Swiss army knife."

He looked back at the ground. The tracks led off through the bog. Leaving the sodden blanket behind him, his face set with a determination he had never known, Jonathan followed.

He came upon them suddenly, and knew instinctively that it had not been much of a fight. The foliage was blackened, trunks still smouldering from the intense fire which had briefly blazed, even in the wet conditions. For a minute, he thought he was going to be sick. Then he *was* sick, supporting himself against a tree, retching into the undergrowth. He had nothing in his stomach. The "meal" which he had received two hours ago had gone directly into his bloodstream. He wiped his mouth with his armoured forearm, tasting acid. He looked again, this time with greater care, and counted the bodies. Nineteen bodies lay on the smouldering ground, burnt beyond recognition. One was missing.

He still couldn't fathom the utter destruction. The armour – even the power shields which Kristiana had given them – had been useless against the thing that had attacked them. In some cases, the blackened bones of the troopers lay exposed to the air. To his untrained eyes, it looked as if they had been taken by surprise. He sniffed a little, studying his own armour with renewed interest. "Swiss army knife it might be. But it won't stand up against a direct attack. I think I'll try to avoid that."

He walked around the scene, trying to ignore the smell of roast meat. He was close, he knew it. He focused the whorl, the sights of his weapon, as carefully he surveyed the area. Above, the sky was clear. No danger there. The foliage still enclosed him, mocking the site of the attack with its stillness. He surveyed the area once again. Ahead of him, through the dense undergrowth, the land rose almost vertically. He couldn't see the top of it through the foliage.

The light from the two suns angled sharply through the trees. Sunset, he thought. Just great. Somehow, I don't feel like getting stuck out here with no light. Then he noticed the first touches of red in the sky overhead, and knew that the Red Giant was rising, and would once again be lighting this land. He knew that there would be no night. "What a day," he said to no one in particular. He looked back at the grim scene on the forest floor. "And it's going to get longer." He put his head down, then, trudging through the mud towards the huge embankment that stretched out in front of him.

23

Barnabus had been working for twenty hours without a break. The sweat rolled down his face, gathering for a moment in the hairs of his moustache, then dripping to the ground. Absently, he wiped it away. The room was littered with the notes he had taken from his overcoat. An assortment of machine parts lay scattered in a corner. In his hurry, he had tried to organise them into some sort of order, but had not really succeeded. He was too concerned about getting the project under way.

As he worked, he mumbled. "Let's see. That diode goes . . . where?" He grabbed a diagram from a pile, studying it intently, then placed the fine wires on the circuit board. He applied the soldering iron briefly. He studied it for a second. "Not bad, I guess. Not bad at all, all things considered."

The mechanism lay in front of him, a box only two foot square. It was a mishmash of electrical parts, with red, blue, black and white wires running over it, out of it, through it. He studied it again, allowing himself a brief smile. "Who would ever have thought that a lowly secondary school Maths teacher would have thought this through!" He laughed a little. "But then, what was it that Mrs Lowell, our English teacher, always said? 'Pride goeth before a fall.'" Still, he couldn't help feeling a tingle of satisfaction, and reached out, patting the little box with a pudgy hand.

"You're finished, then?"

He started, turning to see behind him. Traun blocked the door, arms folded around his waist. Barnabus sighed a little.

"You might knock, Traun. It is the polite thing to do, after all."

Traun only grunted. "Kristiana is waiting."

"Well, tell her divine imperial majesty . . . " He stopped, reconsidering. "Sorry, I get a little caught up when I'm engaged in a project. Tell . . . Kristiana . . . that I'm almost finished."

"Good. We do not have much time."

"Any idiot would know that." Barnabus tried to control his anxiety level. "Yes," he replied more evenly. "I've felt the tremors. They seem to be getting closer."

Traun nodded stiffly. "Borgnoff is homing in on us even as we speak."

"And when It finds us? What then? Immediate destruction, I suppose."

Traun shrugged. "Perhaps. Perhaps not. Sometimes, It plays games. We shall see when the time comes." He clasped Barnabus firmly on the shoulder. "But that is not for you to worry about. For now, you worry about your little machine."

Barnabus nodded shortly. "Fine. Leave me in peace for another hour – that's a standard terrestrial hour, by the way – and I should have it finished." Traun remained, motionless. "Can't you understand, Traun? Go away for a bit!"

The old warrior said nothing, just turned to leave. Barnabus called after him. "Traun, just a moment. Do you know where Cathy and Jonathan are? I haven't seen them about."

Traun turned back to the teacher. "They are gone."

"Gone?"

"Yes, they have gone with Psorsis. Against orders, you understand."

"I beg your pardon. Did you say they had gone? Gone out? Outside into . . . " the room rocked with a detonation just above their heads, " . . . into that!" Barnabus blustered about the room, grabbing his coat and a few notes. "This is out of the question! Jonathan, what do you think you're doing! Unforgivable. And Cathy. You'd think she'd have more sense! Wait until I get my hands on them. They won't forget. Oh, no. Not likely!" He walked up to the large immovable object standing at the doorway. "Come on, Traun! Don't just stand there. I want some action."

"I do not understand."

"We're going to see Kristiana. Something has to be done to get those incorrigible teenagers back in here."

"It is not possible."

He stood firmly, looking directly into the eyes of his adversary. "I say it is!"

"It is your function to finish your machine."

"That's fine. But I will not finish it until we've spoken to Kristiana." Barnabus stood there, arms crossed, his face a moustached mask.

Traun studied him for only a moment. "Then we must do it quickly."

"Oh we will, Traun, we will!"

"No, we will not send anyone else out. You have no idea what it's like out there." Kristiana stood ramrod-straight as a twenty-year-old. Barnabus still had trouble fathoming her actual age. Intellectually, it was interesting. But the thought of living over five thousand years!

"God," he thought, "I wonder if it gets boring . . . " He shook himself slightly, trying to get back on track. "And I say you must, Kristiana! Jonathan and Cathy are my charges. I am responsible for them. I simply must insist on finding them."

"And I say that for the present, at least, it is impossible."

He looked at her, eyes cold, choosing his words carefully. "Anything is possible. You of all people must know that."

She nodded. "I understand your feelings. Even at my great age, while I can no longer consider myself quite . . . human, I too can feel compassion." She turned from him, her figure catching the light, reflecting it as if she were made of glass. "It is what I've devoted my life to: compassion for my people. For thousands of years, my son and I have devoted ourselves to the revitalisation of the culture of Atlantis. You do not know to what heights our culture had climbed thousands of years ago." She smiled at him coldly. "Nor what we have been reduced to."

"I have seen some proof of your former glory."

"Of course. The monument on Earth. Then perhaps you can appreciate what we have accomplished. Thousands of years ago, our people fled your planet. We left because of the evil one, Borgnoff." She spat it out, contemptuously. "It was the one who destroyed the original Atlantis. As easily as I might kill an insect."

"Do you know why?"

She laughed sharply. "No. Even after all these years, we do not know. We can guess, of course. We believe that It was envious. Envious of our intelligence, our capabilities. Perhaps It believed that we would one day pose a threat to It. It matters little, now. In the days of my grandfather It attacked. Without warning and without provocation. It destroyed our civilisation." She smiled briefly. "Well, almost all of it. A few people left Atlantis prior to its destruction. My uncle was one of them and he established a village in the Place of the Sun, where he started work on the monument."

"You know, of course, that I've been there. We call it Newgrange."

She smiled briefly. "It is good that it survives still. It was built as a tribute to Psorsis and to protect his scrolls. It is right that it should survive." She thought for a moment. "This Borgnoff left us alone for two generations. But in my generation, It attacked again. We attempted to put up a defence, but Its power was too great. We knew that we must evacuate in order to protect our culture. We did not take everyone. Some of our citizens fled at the first attack. They chose to stay on the world which you call Earth." She gazed at Barnabus. "They survived, of course. Even now, their blood courses through the veins of the people who live there."

Barnabus returned her gaze, startled for a moment. "You mean *our* blood?"

"How would it be otherwise? We are related, you and I. Oh, I'll admit, not very closely. But Atlantean blood flows through your veins. And through those of your fellows. This is good. The people of Atlantis have left a legacy behind, however humble."

She thought for a moment. "So, now the blood of Atlantis has been re-united. This is good, also, for we need help. I can't tell you how difficult it is to say that. We have many powers, Barnabus. We have used the scrolls which my grandfather left to us many times. With his knowledge, we have developed our minds a hundredfold. We have built huge cities by understanding the nature of metals. We have learned to tap the powers of this planet. Those powers have helped us to build a civilisation of which even Psorsis would have been proud.

"Yet, we are not a warring nation. We have never understood the need to build weapons for defence." Kristiana smiled, just a little. "My son, Psorsis always warned me. Such weapons as we have were developed at his bidding. He believed that we should build more but I would not listen. O that I had . . . ."

"Now, Borgnoff has found us again. Now, it seems, It intends to finish the job which It began many thousands of years ago." Kristiana's face was set. "This time, we may not survive."

Barnabus nodded. "I understand, Kristiana. It is indeed terrible what you face. What we all face. But you must understand my needs. Cathy and Jonathan are not yet adults. I am responsible for them. Surely, you must let me find them."

She stood for a moment, again considering his request. Slowly, she shook her head.

Traun didn't bother to announce himself, which was in itself unusual. He ran through the door, stopping directly in front of his leader. "Kristiana, I apologise, but I felt that you should know at once."

She looked at him, at once knowing, and dreading what she knew. "Psorsis," she said.

Traun nodded. "Borgnoff has destroyed them."

"The energy field did nothing to protect them?"

He bowed his head in front of Kristiana. "Nothing. Its power burned right through it."

"And Psorsis? What of him?"

Traun looked directly into the eyes of his leader. "We believe that Borgnoff has taken him. Alive."

Kristiana shuddered, turning away. Barnabus looked at Traun. "And what of Jonathan and Cathy? Any sign of them?"

"No, nothing yet."

Barnabus turned to Kristiana. "Now, perhaps, you will reconsider? For your son's sake?"

She paused, ancient emotions racking her body. "Yes," she whispered finally, "I will reconsider."

24

The climb was difficult. The great red sun played on him, and sweat streamed off his face, plastering his hair to his forehead. He raised his hand, flicking the dripping water from his eyes. The dark protective armour which covered his body glinted in the sunlight. His skin felt cool underneath the alien material, and he grinned suddenly, grateful for the Atlanteans' technology. "God knows they could use something like this in the Sahara," he grunted. He looked up the hill. It stretched up overhead, at least another two hundred metres.

Jonathan sighed, and kept climbing.

For a long time, he climbed through reddish-brown vegetation. Broad leaves slapped at his face, slowing his progress. Then the undergrowth ended. In front of him, as far as he could see, the ground was barren, scorched. Bare rock lay in a tumble, blackened from intense heat. Tentatively, he put out a hand. The surface of a boulder crumbled into sand. "Unbelievable," he whispered to himself. "What kind of weapon does this Borgnoff have?" He looked up the incline, sweating now not from the heat, but from fear. Slowly, he surveyed the rocky jumble in front of him, his weapon sight looking for a target, any target. "Nothing," he said to himself. "Come on, Jonathan. Another couple of hundred metres, and we've made it." He looked at the blackened powder which he held. "Come to think of it, now's a good time to go home, if I'm going to go. Why did I ever take Cathy to Barnabus's house in the first place?" He threw the sand to the ground, and started climbing again.

It took him another hour to climb up the unstable surface. Once he slipped on the pulverised rock, tumbling ten or fifteen feet, only to come up short against a huge boulder which had somehow survived the onslaught. The suit protected him from the worst of the impact, but he sat for a moment, taking an energy injection from the Atlantean survival kit. He could feel the nutrients flow through him and he rose to start again.

Finally he stood before a sheer face of rock. He studied it for a moment, working out his strategy. He reached out for one handhold, then another. He put his hand up again, and he felt a flat surface. He knew that he had reached the top. Carefully, now, he secured his footing and, reaching up, hauled himself to the top. For a moment he lay still, holding himself there, his arms shaking with the effort. He had no desire to go further. Not towards what he saw on the other side of the ledge.

A great white plain spread out in front of him, like an Arctic wasteland. It stretched as far as he could see, flat and featureless. Except for one element which was directly in front of him, only a mile or so from where he clung to the burned granite ledge. And it was so foreign to him that he thought for a moment that he was hallucinating.

From the middle of the plain of white, a huge globe rose into the sky, hundreds of metres high. As he watched, bright nodules of light danced along its surface, moving about it like some sort of strange parasites. And from the top of the globe, a spear of pulsating red light stretched up, reaching up through the atmosphere, up to where it finally touched the inferno of the red sun.

"Slow down, will you!" Barnabus ran along behind them, coat flapping, doing his best to keep up. The going had been rough for the old mathematics teacher. It was bad enough that he had to keep dodging white-hot spears of light, but it was repugnant to his very soul that he had yet again to slog through a muddy swamp which coated him with putrid-smelling slime. But standing at the bottom of a cliff, gazing upwards, and knowing that he had to climb to the top – that was the last straw.

"I am definitely not climbing this. Students or no students, it is just not possible."

Traun turned to him, his face reflecting the low red light of the setting sun. He smiled acidly. "I would remind you that pursuing your charges was your suggestion," he stated mildly.

"So it was. So it was." Barnabus shuffled slightly, sitting on a rock, putting a hand to his head. "At my age, I should be at home reorganising my files. Or at least writing my memoirs. Not gallivanting through some hostile, alien forest!" He looked up. The climb, he knew, was beyond him. "Jonathan and Cathy are my responsibility. I know that. And if anything happened to them . . . " He looked at Traun glumly. "It would fall on my head, I know that." He looked again up the steep incline. "You're certain that they're up there?"

Traun nodded. "Yes. My people have been tracking them. We now know that Borgnoff has taken the girl as well as Psorsis."

"Cathy has been taken?" His face drained of blood. "If anything has happened to her . . . "

"Be at peace. We know that she is alive. She is with Psorsis."

Barnabus rose. "Well, that's certainly a relief." He said it bitterly. "I suppose that being with Psorsis guarantees her safety." He walked towards the old Atlantean. "I'm no fool, Traun. Do you think that I overlooked the bodies of your warriors back there? I counted nineteen. Nineteen blackened corpses. Not even your powers, however significant, could protect them. Am I now to believe that the presence of Psorsis will somehow shield Cathy from death?" Barnabus turned his back on him. "I have never seen the like of the powers of this . . . this intelligence. Certainly, you have no ability to defeat such a force."

"Ah, but we do. The scrolls of Psorsis."

"But you haven't got the scrolls! You lost them when your back was turned."

"That is true. But it is possible that Psorsis may escape. With some luck, he may still be able to bring back the scrolls. And if he succeeds, we shall be there to protect him."

"And if he is unsuccessful?"

Traun looked at him, his face impassive. "Then, after seven thousand years, the fellowship of Atlanteans shall cease to exist."

He considered. "And Jonathan? What of Jonathan?"

Traun did not look at him. "We have not been able to locate him."

"Which means he *may* be dead." Barnabus felt his eyes welling. "But still, we have Cathy and Psorsis to consider."

"And the survival of my race."

"Yes. Your people." He looked again up the great incline before him. "Well, I guess that there's nothing left for it but to climb the bloody hill."

Jonathan scurried over the ledge, hiding for a moment behind a mass of boulders. Slowly, he raised his head, looking briefly at the scene in front of him. The white plain stretched out in all directions.

"Doesn't look like anything's going on," Jonathan whispered to himself. He looked again at the weird structure which rose in front of him. "They wouldn't have brought her to that. And if they did bring her there, how on Earth am I going to get into that thing?" He shook his head and sighed. "Well, if I'm going to go, I'd better get on with it. Damn Cathy, anyway. How does she manage to get me into these things?"

Jonathan crawled out from behind the rough shelter, stumbling awkwardly down the shallow incline. The surface here was a mass of rubble, blackened too by the forces that had created the vast plain in front of him. His dark suit matched the rock almost perfectly. Great camouflage here, he thought. But how am I going to cross that sea of white?

Now, the slope levelled. Only metres away from him, the boulders stopped. Just stopped. As if a giant had cut them with a knife. Beyond this demarcation, the plain stretched out to the horizon. He saw now that what appeared to be white paint was really the dust of a trillion tonnes of rock and earth, pulverised into near nothingness. Certainly, the structure rising in front of him had been responsible for the destruction. "Maybe it used the surrounding countryside as material for its own construction," he said absently. Except for the strange network of light towering in the distance, the plain was empty. Or so he thought.

Looking out into it, past the glowing target whorl that danced in front of him, he thought he saw movement. He wiped the sweat from his eyes, looking more carefully. "Nothing. Just a mirage, I guess," he muttered to himself. Then, it appeared again. A glint of light. Nothing more. In the darkening gloom of the planet, it stood out briefly, just on the horizon, twinkling like starlight. He watched. It moved suddenly, dancing toward him. Stopping, as if taking its bearings. Then another appeared. And another. Now there were ten, twenty. Maybe a hundred of them, moving up over the horizon. One second, a glint in the distance. The next second, halfway toward him. Moving constantly. And always toward him.

"I don't know what they are. But whatever they are, I don't like the look of them." He looked around, trying to find a place to hide. To his left, fifty metres away, boulders had been piled on top of each other, forming a natural shelter. "Well, it's not exactly a high-tech fortress, but it will have to do." He peeped out from his hiding place. "Right. Now when I say go, run like hell." The pinpoints of light moved steadily toward him. "Now!" He stood up, running across the broken rubble. He looked back over his shoulder. The lights were closer now. Converging on him from every direction. He didn't know what he would do when he got to the rocks. He had some notion that he might try to burrow into the crevasses between the rocks. From there, he would shoot anything that tried to move toward him. The rocky pile was only metres away, towering over him. Quickly, he scrambled around to the far side.

In the gloom, he almost fell into a deep shaft. It was sunk vertically into the ground and perfectly round, maybe ten metres across. For some reason it was drawing in air. Dust eddies whorled about its edges, being drawn down into the darkened pit. He squatted, looking down into it then back toward the huge network of light. "Must be some sort of air-duct," he muttered. "If it is, it probably goes directly into the structure." He looked down into it again. From where he stood, he couldn't see the bottom. He looked quickly behind him. The lights were almost on him. "Now what do I do?"

He thought about jumping. But he didn't know what he was jumping into. He didn't know how deeply the shaft was sunk. For all he knew, he might fall a mile before finding the end. Pretty messy way to end this little outing, he thought. He stood, looking down the shaft, uncertain.

The light came out from behind the rock jumble. It must have been a scout, looking for him. He saw it only briefly. The light was startling, illuminating the ground around it. It was only as big as a man's head. The light originated from its centre, from the maze of tiny sparks that criss-crossed back and forth.

Quickly, he pointed the whorl sight on it. His thumb touched the palm of his hand. The power flowed through him. Up out of the ground, through his legs and chest. Focusing in front of his eyes. Then discharging.

The thing in front of him seemed to absorb the power for a moment. Then, the globe of light expanded, growing to three times its size. Jonathan ducked. The explosion knocked him off his feet. Rock tumbled into the hole, falling out of sight. Jonathan looked up. The thing was gone. Blown out of existence.

"I guess that's one way of getting rid of them." He looked around. A hundred points of light moved toward him, homing in on the blast. Jonathan got to his feet, looking down into the hole. The lights were only a hundred metres away.

"By God, I hope you're worth it, Cathy." He closed his eyes and jumped.

25

She regained consciousness slowly. Her eyes flickered and she saw light. But for a moment, she wanted to close them again, to let herself sink back to wherever she had been. This is one crazy dream, she thought, over and over again. Any second now, I'll wake up. Go downstairs to breakfast. Walk down the hill to class. And then, of course, she would get to see Jonathan.

She dreamed a little about Jonathan. I guess he's nice. Pretty awkward at times. And he never does get it right in maths. Well, maybe that's not true. He needs help, that's all. Cathy smiled in her dreaming. He has nice eyes, she thought. And good strong shoulders. Maybe, when I see him next, I'll say something to him . . .

"Jonathan!" she said quietly, urgently, now remembering. The last time I saw Jonathan . . . he was running toward me. Running. And I . . . I was going up. Rising above him. I saw him. Trying to get to me. But I couldn't move. Couldn't do anything . . .

Remembering, she woke and opened her eyes fully. What she saw made her wish that she had kept them closed. She hung, suspended in space. Her arms and legs vibrated slightly, splayed out from her body. She looked, but she couldn't see how she was held. A faint pulsing of light encircled her. Held her fast in its grip.

She looked around her. A vast network of light shimmered around her, forming a great sphere stretching in all directions.

It was as if she was held at its nucleus. She was trapped in a vast ball of power and light. Occasionally, a small node of bright white light moved quickly along the network, traversing it from one horizon to another. Sometimes, two nodes would meet, stopping to touch, as if to share information, then move on across the sphere.

Directly above her, it became more interesting. Here, red light seemed to pour into the shimmering globe, its intensity almost blinding. A red sun lit this strange planet! Occasionally, a light would arc from this source of power to touch the other elements of the network; light and noise simultaneous; a smell of ozone drifting down to her. She watched the fingers of light and she recognised them, fear coursing through her belly. These were the same bolts of power which had wrecked the city of the Atlanteans.

Cathy watched, mystified. She knew that she was observing a vast intelligence, but an intelligence which was incredibly dangerous. She realised that she lived because this network of power deemed it suitable – at any second, It might change Its – mind.

She looked again at the huge labyrinth of power. A mind. That's what it reminded her of. She hung inside the consciousness of a great mentality. Yet why did It need her?

She wrestled for a moment with the forces that gripped her. They held fast. Then she realised that she depended greatly on them. If they let go, or if she were able to break free, she would fall. Below, many, many metres below, the network of light continued its path. She had no doubt what dropping into the labyrinth would mean. Like a fly hitting a hot wire. One zzzzttt! and no more Cathy.

Certainly, there must be some means of escape. Come on, she thought, think!

She was interrupted. As she looked directly in front of her, she saw a group of bright motes which seemed to be playing, coalescing, turning, becoming one larger light, then moving out into separate entities again. They played for a while more, but now, they seemed to be building something. Slowly, a flickering network of light grew within them. They spun crazily, and the light leapt toward her, a bridge between the sides of the globe and where she hung suspended.

They crossed the bridge slowly, carrying something dark within them. They were almost on her, their light blinding. In their midst, they carried a man. She watched as they hung him beside her, energising the atmosphere, and she could see it catch at his arms and legs, holding him there. He hung suspended beside her; a little above her. Their job complete, the motes moved back across the bridge of light.

She looked up at the man. She knew him. "Psorsis. Psorsis?" She whispered it at first, afraid to be heard. The man did not stir. She called a little louder. "Psorsis?"

"I hear you." His words were bound with pain. Slowly, he moved his head, his eyes opening. "So, little one, they have you, too."

"Yes, they have me. But if I have anything to do with it, it won't be for long."

Psorsis grimaced, his face a mask of pain. "Don't be too certain. Here, they do with you as they please."

"I don't understand why they captured me. Why didn't they just kill me and get it over with?"

"They think that you know."

"Know? Know what?"

He looked at her, his eyes wide. "The truth that the scrolls hold."

She shook her head slightly. "But they have the scrolls. What do they want with me? Or with you either, for that matter?"

Psorsis smiled, his face less tense. "Borgnoff may have the scrolls. But for all Its intelligence, It does not understand them. It can never understand them. If It did, it would spell the end of everything. Do you see?"

"No, I don't see."

Psorsis whispered. "The scrolls have the power of the universe within them. With these secrets, this intelligence, this Borgnoff would rule everything. It would destroy everything."

He turned in pain. "We cannot divulge the scrolls' secrets."

Cathy smiled grimly. "That's easy enough, considering I don't know anything about them. Why don't I just tell them that, and we'll get out of here."

He smiled at her briefly. "You are innocent. You think they will simply take your word. It is not that easy. Borgnoff does not simply ask. Often, It takes. See how It tried to take from me."

Psorsis moved his head. Turning so that she could see. The back of his skull had been removed. From where she hung, Cathy could see the cortex of his brain; see the blood coursing through the main arteries; see the grey mass move slightly as Psorsis shivered in pain.

She screamed, not caring who heard.

The shaft must have been at least five metres deep. Jonathan hit hard, falling on his side. He lay for a minute in the gloom, trying to get his breath. Light from the nodes filtered down, bathing his face in their glow. He thought that they were coming after him, but at that moment – Cathy or no Cathy – he really didn't care. "The things I go through for this girl," he muttered. He looked back up the shaft. Lights orbited over the shaft, and he sat, waiting, his weapon sight focused on the opening. He wouldn't be able to destroy them all. He knew that. There were too many. He had never thought much about death. But now, sitting in the dirt at the bottom of the pit, he thought that death was likely. OK, he thought, if you're going to do it, do it. But let's get it over quick. He waited. Nothing happened. The lights swarmed above him, and then, one by one, began to drop out. They were leaving. He didn't know why. The shaft darkened. The lights were gone. Only the faint glow of the setting Red Giant filtered into the shaft.

Jonathan looked around. In front of him was an opening. Not large. Maybe a metre high. He should start walking, of course. But what lay on the other side? That was the real question. Jonathan considered his options, but realised he didn't have any. He could forget about climbing out of the shaft. The walls had no handholds, and he could hardly jump five metres. And even if he could climb out, God alone knew what might greet him. "Anyway you look at it, I lose," he said.

He crawled over to the opening, staring into it. "No light," he muttered. "Terrific." He got to his feet. Considering that he had jumped fifteen feet, he felt all right. "Nothing broken, I guess." He brushed the dirt from his suit, at the same time peering into the darkness of the tunnel. "Whatever's down there, here I come." He lowered his head, bent down and started walking.

In the gloom he lost his sense of time and of direction. He walked a long way. One, maybe two kilometres. The dimensions of the tunnel made him walk hunched over. His back and neck hurt and his legs ached. He reckoned that he was heading towards the sphere. After all, he didn't know anywhere else of interest in the immediate vicinity.

Jonathan did his best to keep his head up, trying to keep the weapon-sight pointed directly in front of him. At any second, he anticipated that something unexpected would pop out in front of him, and he wanted to give whatever it was a surprise. "Might as well shoot first if I get the chance." Jonathan shivered involuntarily, whether from fear or cold, he didn't know. "It sure is dark in here," he muttered to himself. "I hate the dark. Wish somebody would turn on the lights."

He hobbled on for what seemed like hours. The tunnel ran in a straight line, making the way easier. Then it began to curve upwards. At first, the climb was imperceptible, and Jonathan thought that he was only tiring. However, as the incline became steeper, he knew that the tunnel was taking him up towards the surface. He looked in front of him. In the distance, he could make out a faint glow. His eyes, adjusted to the darkness, could now see the curving path in front of him. "I might have unwelcome company soon." He paused, crouched, hands on knees, to rest and consider. "Slowly, now, Jonathan. Take it slowly."

He dropped on to his belly, and started to crawl up the incline. The light in front of him grew in intensity. The tunnel seemed to be narrowing a little. The breeze grew stronger, eddying around him, cooling his face. He could see an opening. It shone like a rising sun, sending light deep into the tunnel. Jonathan placed the whorl of his weapon sight directly in the centre of the opening, his thumb moving over the firing mechanism on his palm. If anything moved, he'd fire first and make any apologies later. Slowly, he moved up the tunnel, inching his way forward, only ten metres away from the opening . . . only five . . . now only a metre. He stopped, looking out across an open space.

"Holy . . . !" he whispered, his voice hoarse with fear, ducking back below the surface. Lying in the tunnel, he peered out on a vast network of moving lines, a white network of energy that pulsated like a living heart. His field of vision was blocked by the walls of the tunnel. He had to see more. Carefully, he inched his way forward.

Now, he could see an entire horizon of glowing lines. As he watched, he recognised the nodes of white light, brothers to the ones that had chased him on the surface. Here, they seemed attached to the lines of energy, moving to a series of commands.

He rolled over on his back, trying to get a better view. It was then that he saw them. Suspended above him hung two figures. Instantly, he recognised who they were. "Cathy," he gasped quietly. "And Psorsis." They dangled in mid-air. He couldn't see anything supporting them; couldn't see any way of getting to them. "I've found you. Now I have to find a way to get you out of here."

He lay still, trying to develop a plan. Any plan. The nodes of light went on about their business, seeming not to detect his presence. Jonathan scanned the network of glowing lights, looking for a way up to Cathy. It didn't look good. He saw other openings similar to the one in which he rested. Every fifty metres or so, the network was interrupted with such an opening. He thought for a moment that there might be more, higher up, closer to Cathy and Psorsis. He didn't see any. "Maybe I could find a way to the top of the globe. Then figure out how to let myself down to her."

Jonathan shifted, looking up to the very apex of the structure. From his position, Jonathan could see that the network converged in a circle of glowing red. He knew that this was where the great red cord touched the globe, attaching it tenuously to the Red Giant which hung many thousands of kilometres above them. It made him shudder. The energy which it tapped must be incredible. As he watched the circle of red, it began to change, glowing brighter, expanding as it did so. Now, it appeared to consume the network of light in its path, seeming to absorb it, consuming the energy in front of it. That was not the only change. A number of the nodes of white light crawled up the pathways as if grasped by the power in front of them. He watched one as it moved toward the red circle, gathering speed, now hurtling along its pathway, and finally plunging into the growing red substance. As it did so, it disintegrated, a bright flash and faint rumble marking its destruction. Others followed, and Jonathan watched as white explosions pock-marked the surface of the growing red nemesis.

Jonathan saw more and more of the nodes sail up the globe, onward to their doom. With each explosion, the diameter of the red object grew, as if feeding on the energy which the nodes released. Relentlessly, it moved out from the apex, growing to fill the huge structure, descending towards Cathy, who hung helplessly in its path.

He was out of time. He had to get to Cathy, but still didn't have a plan.

A light flashed at the tunnel's entrance. Carefully, Jonathan moved forward, head now exposed. He looked down, watching as one of the lights travelled along one of the pathways, up toward the giant of red. The pathway of light was directly below him, only an arm's length away. Here, the great globe had buried itself into the earth. The stone was fused into walls of what appeared to be glistening ceramic. The pathways seemed to stand away from the stone, suspended above the ground.

Because there were no walls, the air seemed to shimmer. He now saw why the globe was opaque. Energy from the network paths was constantly being discharged. The electrons in the air between them, excited by the energy discharge, glowed, too, forming a solid wall of light.

To his eyes, the pathway looked solid enough. As if the light was being discharged from a solid source of energy. It was at least a metre wide. Wide enough, he thought. Tentatively, Jonathan put out one of his hands, ready to back away. "A little closer," he whispered. "Closer . . . " He stretched, grunting at the effort. "With my luck, I'll electrocute myself." He reached a little further. He touched it, withdrawing his hand immediately.

Nothing happened. The suit must be insulating me somehow, he thought. Carefully, he reached out again, this time pressing the palm of his hand down on the glowing surface. It was solid. He left his hand there for a moment. Vaguely, he could feel warmth through the lining of his armour but that was all.

For the first time in a long time, Jonathan smiled. He looked up at Cathy, and at the other figure dangling above him. "I'm coming for you, Cathy, don't worry." Jonathan crawled out from the tunnel, and stood, exposed for all to see, a tiny black figure on a background of purest white light.

26

The search-and-rescue party moved quickly up the hill, fifteen men at arms, all wearing the black flexible armour, all encased in the shimmering protective shield which Kristiana had generated for them. Over their shoulders, ten of them carried long cylindrical tubes, with the gold symbol of the whorl of Atlantis burnished on the sides. They moved in an orderly fashion, making good time as they climbed over the large rocks embedded in the side of the hill. All, that is, except Barnabus. He struggled at the back, trying to keep up. His brown overcoat, stained and torn, rippled as he climbed wearily up the rock formations. He stopped for a moment, leaning against a boulder, trying to get his breath. One of the warriors looked back, yelling something which was lost in the wind. He rose again, wrapping the coat around him, and resumed the long trudge up the hill.

They came to the ledge. Fourteen of them squatted, waiting as one of their number levered himself slowly over the lip. He paused for a moment, uncertain. He turned briefly, uttering instructions. They moved quickly over the ledge, hiding behind the huge rock formations that dotted the summit of the hill. The lone figure sat waiting, looking up. One of the black-suited soldiers reached back over the lip, grabbing the outstretched arm, pulling him up over the edge.

The two of them sat for a moment, breathing hard. Barnabus looked up, and what he saw made him shudder. The soldier rose slightly, grabbing him by the shoulder. Roughly, he shoved him ahead until they reached cover behind one of the boulders. Using hand signals, the soldier communicated with the rest of the troops. Stealthily, they started moving down the hill.

"You can't really believe that you're going to get them out of there." They had stopped again, hiding behind the boulders, only a few metres from where the white plain began its stretch across the planet. Barnabus was tired, his muscles quivered with exhaustion. He squinted into the sun, now low on the horizon. The huge globe, its network of lights pulsating ominously, burned in the twilight. The ribbon of light curved from its top, moving towards the horizon, out towards its meeting place with the Red Giant. It burned an angry red, distended at the top of the globe, seeming to eat its way into the core of the glowing network. Around the globe, hundreds of points of light hovered ominously, as if guarding against any attack.

Traun sat on his haunches, eating from his day-pack. He closed the pack, and stowed it into a pocket. "Kristiana has given me orders to get them out. I will obey my orders."

"You're certain they're in there?"

"Of course they are. We still aren't certain where the girl is; all we know is that she was taken. She was not wearing a suit. Psorsis was wearing one. We think the boy was wearing one, too. Our equipment allows us to track anyone wearing a suit. Now, it shows two men inside." He pointed to the structure glowing in front of them. "Of interest is the fact that one of the men seems to be moving towards the other, who is stationary. We can only guess that your boy somehow obtained a suit and that he was then captured by Borgnoff. We believe that Psorsis has broken free, and is trying to rescue Jonathan."

"And how do you intend to help with the rescue?"

Traun smiled woodenly. "You will see, old man. Just keep out of the way." Traun looked at the horizon. Energy seemed to be pulsing down the red ribbon of light; power robbed from the Red Giant hanging just above the horizon. As they watched, the ribbon began to grow in diameter as if storing even more power. It darkened into a deep ugly red; flashes of lightning, power excess to its needs, discharged, striking the white ground surrounding the globe. "We cannot wait much longer. It is time."

The old warrior checked his suit, then looked closely at his personal field of energy which shimmered around him. When he was satisfied that he was ready, he put his hand up. His men saw the signal and checked their own defences. When they were all satisfied, each returned the signal. Now, Traun dropped his arm, and the troops started to run on to the flat of the white plain. To Barnabus, it seemed certain suicide. He waited for a moment, uncertain. Then, lifting the edges of his old coat, he began to stumble along behind.

They did not run far, only forty or fifty metres. Traun led, running next to one of the cylinder carriers. When they had gone far enough, Traun put up his arm. Each cylinder was placed upright on the white ground, forming a circle perhaps twenty metres wide. The men holding them placed their palm on the burnished whorl of the cylinder. Within, they could hear the low rumbles, the vibration as the machines came alive. They stood back, waiting. Slowly, the cylinders cut their way into the ground, disappearing into the earth a few centimetres a second.

Traun knew that he didn't have much time. It would take almost a full sixty seconds for the mechanisms to work and already Borgnoff had seen them. In the distance, the group of white nodes started to vibrate, now moving forward, searching.

Traun looked back, issuing another hand signal. Behind each of the ten cylinders, the men dropped to their knees, looking toward the oncoming nodes of light.

There were hundreds of them. Traun aimed his vision sights on the first. It was just out of range, uncertain where the threat was, flitting back and forth as it searched for its prey. Traun filed the information for future use. Obviously, its master was not infallible. It did not have a good targeting system.

The node of light must have picked up something for it was coming closer. It was only fifty metres away. Traun could see its bright centre as it came towards him. He put up his hand. His men froze.

The node of light swept past him, not noticing. Then it came back, locking on to him. The light sat centred in the middle of his whorled weapon site. The thing saw him and it moved forward, moving so quickly that Traun almost didn't have time to react.

He touched his thumb to his palm. The energy focused in front of him for an instant, then moved at the speed of light, obliterating his enemy in an explosion which almost knocked him over. He looked around. The other nodes had seen the attack. They were advancing quickly. Time was running out.

He yelled to the man beside him. "How much longer?"

"Ten seconds."

His men braced themselves to meet the attack. Traun picked out his next target, centring the sight. He fired. Again, the explosion. Now, his troops fired at will, fingers of bright light, reaching out to meet the racing globes. They knew that there were too many. But they needed only seconds now.

One of the nodes moved to the side, avoiding Traun's fire. It tacked, making it difficult for its adversaries to get a lock-on. It picked out its target. The soldier to Traun's left didn't have time to shoot.

Kristiana's protection lasted only milliseconds, but it was long enough for the warrior to know his fate. He screamed shortly but then the thing was through, hitting him in the chest, propelling the dart of pure energy through his armour. Death was instantaneous. Millions of volts of energy burned through him, cooking him instantly. Traun watched for a moment. The warrior fell, smoking, to the ground, the node of light still attached to its victim. Busily, it began the work of detaching itself, moving to reach out to its next target. It never had the opportunity. Traun cut it down, the blast blowing the remains of his colleague into a thousand pieces.

The soldier next to him shouted. "It's ready!" Traun stepped back. A hundred nodes descended on them, but it made no difference now. The cylinders had done their work. Traun stretched out his arms, feeling the energy which they held; the energy which came from the core of the planet; from its magnetic fields; from the waters which rolled and crashed hundreds of feet below him. As his ancestors had done before him and as Kristiana had taught him, Traun concentrated his mind. The energy flowed up through the cylinders, into his very being. Carefully, he moulded it, shaped it. He felt the ground beneath him subside as the energy did his bidding. Slowly, almost majestically, the ground sank, and as it did, the sides of the fortress grew, shielding them now from the early threat, grew until it surrounded them. The shimmering energy of the planet, now blue, now red, now white, now gold, became a small fortress designed to buy them time until the strike.

When it was complete, Traun breathed deeply, opening his eyes. His men stood around him, waiting. For a moment, they were safe. But soon, they must make their move. Otherwise, it would be too late. For Psorsis, the visitors, and for them.

He glowered at his troops, grey beard wet with sweat. Then he smiled. In the back, wiping his glasses, Barnabus waited, too. "You asked how we would help," Traun said.

"Yes," Barnabus replied. "I'm beginning to see what you have in mind." He put his glasses back on.

27

The red mass moved closer to them, pulsating, alive. Cathy looked up, seeing the living thing, not believing what she saw. It was huge. A fantastic lesion of matter; controlled energy which threw off great bolts of intense heat as it moved toward her. She struggled but her body was held fast, a tiny insect waiting for the ultimate will of its master.

Psorsis looked at her, his exposed brain wetly reflecting the red light of the energy. "Behold," Psorsis said vehemently. "Behold the treachery of Borgnoff." He looked up to It, and now the nexus of energy halted only metres from where they hung, Its great power now moving rapidly, bright lines of intense light coalescing into circles, into parallel lines, reflecting the vast intelligence which controlled it. Psorsis glared at the pulsating bands of light, hatred overcoming the waves of pain which racked him.

"You!" he quivered. "For centuries you have tried to defeat us. And for centuries, we have refused to be defeated by your hatred."

For a moment, the vastness of energy did not react, the mote of human energy apparently too insignificant to deserve a reply. But now, the white pulses of force dancing within the red mass of energy coalesced again, forming an unblinking nexus. A great doorway to the consciousness of Borgnoff opened to confront the specks of mere human flesh.

Cathy, suspended within the huge cavern, still tried to struggle away from the unfathomable depths of that consciousness. Within her mind, then, she heard it. A whisper only, at first, as that consciousness reached out towards hers. Enveloping her. Capturing her in Its all encompassing grip. Now, she could hear It. The voices of a thousand men screaming. The volume of Its blast threatening to overwhelm her.

YOU HAVE SURVIVED. BUT NO LONGER. YOU ARE NOTHING. YOUR PLANET IS NOTHING. YOU ARE INSIGNIFICANT.

Cathy cringed at Its outburst. "If that is so," she said, "then why can't you leave us all in peace?"

It paused, considering her request. WHILE YOU ARE INSIGNIFICANT, YOU ALSO EXIST. YOUR CIVILISATION EXISTS AND THAT IN ITSELF IS A THREAT. WHILE MY INTELLIGENCE IS HIGH, I UNDERSTAND THE COMPLEXITIES OF YOUR EVOLUTION. I RECOGNISE THAT ONE DAY, YOU MIGHT THREATEN EVEN MY HIGHER EVOLUTIONARY FORM.

Psorsis laughed. "Are you so powerful, then? If you are so powerful, would you destroy a peaceful civilisation? Would you subject us to annihilation? If you are as powerful as you claim to be, my people would pose no threat to you."

YOUR PEOPLE HAVE LONG POSED A THREAT TO ME.

Psorsis nodded. "You speak of my great-grandfather. You speak of the writings which he has left to us. Our birthright. The scrolls of Psorsis."

The nexus of energy again considered. YOUR ANCESTOR KNEW MUCH. EVEN THEN, I WATCHED HIM.

"And you destroyed him!" Psorsis spat.

HAD HE LIVED, HIS POWER WOULD HAVE BEEN AS GREAT AS MY OWN.

"And that's why you stole the scrolls. You tried to interpret them. But even your vast intelligence could not fathom his reasoning. Perhaps," Psorsis looked deeply into the core of corrupted power, "your own evil prevented you from learning from that which Psorsis has left behind."

The wavering bands of light began to rotate again, agitated. Alive with enmity. YOU HAVE SAID ENOUGH. WHAT DO I CARE ABOUT EVIL? I HAVE SEEN GREAT GOODNESS. MY

BROTHERS AND MY SISTERS POSTURED ABOUT GOODNESS, YET THEY PROVIDED ME WITH LITTLE SOLACE. WITH THE KNOWLEDGE OF THE SCROLLS AT MY DISPOSAL, I SHALL BE AS GREAT AS THE OTHER ONES WHO TRAVEL ON THE FAR SIDE OF THE UNIVERSE.

Psorsis smiled slightly, suddenly understanding. "At last, I understand you. You are defective, are you not, Borgnoff? Part of a civilisation devoted to intelligence and understanding, and, perhaps, even love. Somehow, you developed without any of these traits. And because you are deviant," he emphasised the word, "even your own people find you repugnant." Psorsis laughed sharply. "You seek the scrolls," he stated, now knowing, "simply in order to gain more power. Power which you can use to control even your own people. Let me say to you, Borgnoff, that even with this knowledge, you will never be equal, simply because you are a defective. Retarded. A mutation which your own kind has chosen to reject!"

Psorsis's words were heard and understood. Deep within Its intellect and the fractured nature of Its own emotions, the creature called Borgnoff saw Itself fully. It was a defective, tossed out among the seas of the unknown universe like so much flotsam. The anger within It stirred, then grew uncontrolled. Outward. Fuelled from the furnaces of the Red Giant hanging suspended above them. Spewing from the nexus of intelligence as intense heat, scorching the humans held before It.

Cathy heard the next statement in her mind, and tried to scream, but could not, because It held her body in Its grasp.

YOU ARE INSIGNIFICANT. YOU ARE THE DEFECTIVE. SEE WHAT BECOMES OF SUCH DEFECTIVES.

She wanted to look away, but It would not let her. The moving phalanx of light now descended on Psorsis. Touching him lightly on the arm. Entering him there. Psorsis opened his mouth to scream, but his lungs refused to fuel his larynx. As she watched, more rods of light descended towards him, entering him. His body shook violently as the very blood boiled in his veins. His fingernails darkened as the blood there congealed. His face grew mottled, now skin blistered. Now, the air in his lungs was released. The scream, high-pitched, voicing outrage and pain, slapped her almost physically. His eyes moved to hers, begging for help, for release from the pain. As she watched those eyes suddenly collapsed inwards, distorting the face even more, fluid falling now down his cheeks. Dropping away from them to fall into the depths of the alien structure. It was as Borgnoff had said. Psorsis was now a defective. Repugnant to look at.

It was done, now. The fragments of charred tissue were now shrunk over the skeletal remains. Psorsis was no more. Finished, the forces of Borgnoff recombined into their original nexus of pure energy. Slowly, It moved to confront her.

YOU WILL DIE NOW ALSO. YOU WILL DIE OR YOU WILL TELL ME THE SECRETS OF THE SCROLLS.

Catherine could not move. She could not think. She knew that at any moment the flickering lights which were at the core of Borgnoff might touch her too. Might enter her. Her fear cascaded from her very soul, vomiting upward towards the evil which moved slowly towards her.

YOU WILL TELL ME OF THE SCROLLS.

He thinks I understand the scrolls of Psorsis, she thought. As she watched, nodes of light again danced down the network of the intelligence confronting her. Slowly, the bridge of light moved from the walls of the structure surrounding them, moving out towards her. She understood. Borgnoff would read her mind as he had read Psorsis's. The light would remove the top of her cranium. Move into the white matter of her brain as it had to the Atlantean warrior. Again, she tried to scream, but she could not.

The bridge of light was almost to her now. Cathy watched, terrified, as the nodes of light moved out across the bridge of seething power. Now, she could feel the grip holding her relax as the nodes surrounded her. She struggled, kicking out. She knew her fate then, and screamed at last. Her scream was for Jonathan.

28

Jonathan saw the bridge expand slowly out from the edge of the globe. Quickly, he moved up the pathway, his suit shielding him from the inherent forces. He tried to hold himself loose, ready, poised for the attack that he knew would come. His target was set dead-centre on a node blocking the entrance across the bridge. He was almost there, now, running swiftly up the small incline, almost level with Cathy. He looked briefly toward her. She was hitting out in all directions, her face red with fear and anger, dark hair flying above the nodes of light that held her. Beside her, Psorsis hung, still suspended. He didn't move; either he was dead or had passed out.

Still, they didn't see him. Perhaps they ignored him; he didn't know. The red mass continued to contract, moving higher toward the apex of the globe. Rods of light struck out from its centre, impacting against the walls of the globe high above him. As they struck, nodes of light were created. It dawned on Jonathan that the nodes were a part of the thing; that It had used their energy in Its growth, and now It shed them as It again became dormant. He knew, however, that if It saw him, It would send a single arc of energy towards him and that would be that.

He ran faster, moving up the ring of light. He was almost at the junction, the bridge at his level, now, a node blocking his path. He centred the sight, the Atlantean whorl dancing for a minute. He touched his thumb to his palm.

The force coursing through him was different this time and for a moment he thought that his suit had failed. Energy surged through him, up from his feet, enveloping him for a moment in a chrysalis of light. The energy focused, then, a foot in front of him, a ball of power bright blue in its intensity. It flew forward, a sphere of power almost a full metre in diameter. It struck the node dead centre. The node collapsed in on itself. Shrinking in size. Hammered into nothing by the power of his weapon. Jonathan watched. The node simply ceased to exist.

"Wow!" he exclaimed, hoarsely. He knew, then, what had happened. This time, the suit had tapped the power of the globe itself; a structure composed of the materials of the Red Giant hanging above them. He no longer relied on the inner forces of a mere planet. Now, as long as he was in the globe, he had the power of a sun at his disposal.

"Cathy!" He yelled, heard his voice echo in the vastness of the space.

Hearing him, she looked around. "Jonathan! Hurry, for God's sake!" The nodes had halted, a chain of electricity holding the girl in their power. Jonathan looked down. With this huge source of energy, he could destroy them all in one shot from his weapon. But he would kill Cathy, too. He could, of course, try to take them out beneath her. But if he did that, she would fall onto the path. He looked at it, glowing ominously. Cathy wasn't wearing Atlantean armour. If she touched the path, she would die. Or, worse, she would fall. He looked down, seeing the glowing network of light hundreds of metres below them; the great opening leading heaven knew where.

Now Jonathan could feel the power above focusing Its energies on him. He felt It move slowly towards him, into him. He could hear it fastening into his mind.

WHY ARE YOU HERE?

Jonathan looked up. The great circle had stopped contracting. Its single pupil of energy looked down on him, an inhuman eye staring at Jonathan ambivalently.

Jonathan centred the Atlantean weapon sights on the huge nexus of power. If nothing else, he could send a blast of pure energy towards It. He knew that it would probably have no effect. But he wouldn't just sit there waiting for his own extermination. Or Catherine's. God knows if the thing is capable of understanding a reasonable request, he thought. But it's worth a try.

"Look. I just want to take my friend and get out of here. We don't want any trouble."

The circle of energy hung unmoving for a moment. Then, Jonathan heard it.

DO YOU UNDERSTAND THE SCROLLS OF PSORSIS?

Jonathan's eyes narrowed slightly. "You have the scrolls, do you?" he asked.

I HAVE THE SCROLLS.

Jonathan saw them, then. The scrolls, resting in their glass casing, were cantilevered out on a platform of pure energy. He looked at them hungrily, gauging the distance. Twenty metres away? Maybe thirty? How was he supposed to get to them? If he could bring them back somehow, they could defeat this thing. They could go home. All he had to do was rescue Cathy and haul a cubic metre of glass out of here, all the while avoiding the wrath of this sun-sized power-plant.

Jonathan looked up at Borgnoff, hoping that he was acting innocently enough. "OK, my friend. You got me." He swallowed. "I know a little about the scrolls, all right."

YOU KNOW? WHAT DO YOU KNOW?

Jonathan glanced at Cathy, suspended on the bridge of pure energy. "You know. This and that. Some stuff the Atlanteans told me." Good God, he thought. Keep talking. "I know a little about . . . ah . . . universal energy levels. Time and space functions. Quite a bit, come to think of it."

Above him, Cathy had stopped struggling. Her mouth fell open. "Jonathan, for God's sake! What are you saying?"

He moved his hand a little, motioning her to keep her mouth shut. "See? She knows I know." He turned to her slightly. "Come on, Cathy. He's got us. Why don't we just come clean and get out of here."

She lay still for a moment, clutched in the energy fields of the nodes. "Come clean? Come clean?" Her voice moved up an octave. "What are you talking about. This thing is going to kill us! Can't you see? Just look at . . . " she motioned towards Psorsis.

ENOUGH. YOU WASTE TIME. YOU WILL TELL ME NOW WHAT YOU KNOW.

Jonathan noticed then the nodes of light moving down the walls of the globe, moving closer to him. He knew that he was running out of time.

"Hey now," he said weakly. "Come on, you don't expect me to give you what you want just like that. I'll need some reassurances."

YOU SPEAK FOLLY. YOU WILL COME NOW. YOU HAVE NO CHOICE.

He turned a little. He needed more time. He noticed them, then. More lights behind him. He whirled. Three nodes were moving down the path that he was standing on, now only a few feet away. He reacted without thinking.

Ducking down instinctively, he centred his vision and the weapon sights jerked up towards them. Instantly, he pressed thumb to palm. The blue-white arc of light missed at first, crashing instead into the wall of the globe. The impact dislodged the first node. It tumbled from the ledge of energy, falling down into the void. He swept the beam of his weapon ahead, striking the other two. They vapourised in front of him. Quickly, he looked over the side, watching the first node fall helplessly. As it fell, it faded in intensity. Then, it began to skid sideways, falling now toward the gaping opening at the bottom of the globe. Jonathan watched intently. The node seemed to be caught in a vortex of wind; almost a Coriolis

219

effect brought about by the energy as it moved through the network at the bottom of the globe.

The node paused, standing still for a moment in mid-air, as the turbulent atmosphere fought for possession. Then, it fell abruptly, disappearing through the hole.

Jonathan rose slowly, a plan forming in his mind.

Borgnoff roared at him. *YOU!* YOU IMPERTINENT INSECT! NOW, YOU SHALL KNOW THE WRATH OF MY POWER!

Jonathan looked up at the blank white pupil of Borgnoff, watching as it began to spin. Moving quicker and quicker.

"Well," Jonathan said levelly, "if I'm going to do this, I'd better be on about my business. The scrolls first." He turned his eyes to the scrolls, pointing the whorl on the shelf of energy. "Careful," he muttered to himself, "I don't want to vaporise them." He touched his palm. Energy moved up and through him, shooting out now toward the platform. Carefully, he aimed the beam upward. At first, the shelf of energy absorbed the power from his weapon. He stepped forward, concentrating intently. As he watched, the platform began to dissolve. He stopped firing. The scrolls teetered for a moment on the remnants of the shelf. Slowly, the block rocked forward. "Come on!" Jonathan yelled. Then, the scrolls fell, the block tumbling into the void of the globe.

He watched it fall, hoping that the Coriolis would take it, move it into the shaft at the bottom of the globe. The shaft had to be an air-vent, he thought. A super-huge air exchanger that helped to circulate the globe's interior environment. Otherwise, he would be dying of the heat that was dispersed from the sides of the sphere, from its network of energy. He knew that he had crawled into the globe through such an air-exchange unit. That's why he felt the wind as he made his way through the tunnel. His only hope was that the shaft led outside; that anything falling into the hole below him would be transported away from the interior.

He watched as the scrolls of Psorsis tumbled through the void. The thing above him seemed to cough as It watched the scrolls fall; a dull, hollow sound as if a foreign object had lodged in Its throat. Jonathan looked. The pupil was watching the scrolls, now, watching them fall. Focused on them, the pupil dilated, spinning.

Then, the heat moved from It in a fine beam, tracking in on the scrolls, hitting them, the glass casings seeming to fragment, glowing a bright yellow as the glass melted.

"The scrolls!" He yelled it, knowing that this was why they had come; this was the object of their sacrifice, and now they were being destroyed, caught in the energy of Borgnoff.

He turned, his anger immediate, ready to fight the thing above him. He didn't have time. Borgnoff fired, the great bolt of energy catching him unprepared. The suit protected him for a moment, then began to melt in the intense power. He ran forward, glancing at the wound in his left arm. It didn't hurt, not yet, anyway. He tried to ignore his anger; tried to forget the destruction of the scrolls. Jonathan turned his attention to Cathy. She watched him, silent, too shocked to say anything. He winked at her. "See you downstairs," he shouted. He levelled the target sight. The energy from the globe shot through his body, reaching out, centring on the nodes of light which held her. Slowly, they crumbled, releasing her. Cathy fell, arms raised to her face, surrounded by the nodes of light as they, too, fell into the chasm.

One more, Jonathan thought. As he ran, trying to avoid the bolts of power emanating from Borgnoff, he touched his palm, forcing the thumb of his injured arm to work. He focused on a point just above Psorsis, sweeping the power around him, trying to cut through whatever kept him lashed into position. Energy collided with energy, the light intensifying as air molecules became excited, emitting their own light. Psorsis hung for an instant more, then fell free, tumbling head over heels toward the opening below.

Now, Jonathan was free to take care of himself. Nodes of light were in front of him, blocking his path. He fired again, not aiming, hoping that luck would find the targets. He spun. The path was blocked at the other end, more nodes moving up along the path, ready to take him.

He turned, then, to the voice that ridiculed him from above.

"NOW! YOU SHALL PAY! YOU ARE MINE."

The large eye spun once more. Jonathan turned, looking down into the deep pit of the globe.

"Is that so, you bastard! Well, you're just going to have to come and get me." Jonathan jumped, turning, trying to centre his weapon sights on the thing above him. As he did, he saw a great explosion of light, and felt the first wave of concussion. Then all hell broke loose.

29

It had taken them only minutes to mount their attack. Traun stood at the centre of their golden fortress, dictating instructions. His men moved quickly. The main energy transfer unit, a golden box clearly marked with the whorl of Atlantis, was placed in the centre of the fortress. Traun's men were grouped around it, ready to complete their assigned tasks. They stood uneasily, listening as the nodes continued their attack, throwing themselves against the outside of the protective dome. With each attack, they released their energy, attempting to kill. The dome of the fortress glowed bright red as it absorbed the heat, dissipating it harmlessly into the ground.

Traun looked up at Barnabus, his brown teeth showing through in a ragged smile. "You asked what you could do to help? You might pray that this works the way Kristiana planned."

Traun placed his palm on the energy unit's symbol. The box hummed quietly. From its base, white crystals grew, burying themselves into the ground, cutting like a red hot knife through the rock. Their makers could not see the progress, but the crystals grew at a rate of many hundreds of kilometres per hour, moving down, seeking the rich energy of the core of the planet.

Two minutes passed. Then, at the top of the box, a round opening appeared. Barnabus stepped back two paces, watching. At first, nothing happened. Then he noticed a column of air directly above the opening shimmer slightly.

Something was disturbing the atmosphere.

He pointed at the column. "That's a gravitational field, I would guess?"

Traun nodded. "We are tapping the gravitational field of the planet. The field will give shape to the weapon and guide it."

"What weapon?"

Traun smiled grimly. "Watch and see."

Barnabus watched. The column continued to shimmer, now growing more opaque. As it did, the humming from the golden apparatus intensified, increasing its pitch as it moved up an octave, then two octaves. Barnabus put his hands to his ears as the warbling became unbearable.

The ground shook. A small tremor at first, beginning with a low rumble, the box shaking slightly. The men within the dome found it hard to conceal their fear. The rumbling increased. The vibrations were now perceptible, real. Barnabus knelt, steadying himself. Traun looked to his men, his face excited. "Now!" Simultaneously, ten men put their palms on the the the upright columns, touching ten whorls of Atlantis. The shuddering magnified intensely.

From beneath him Barnabus could feel a different movement, as if the ground itself were trying to rise up, releasing the forces contained within it.

He looked towards the column of air. It moved up, touching the top of the glowing dome. As it did, Barnabus felt heat. The ground turned a dull red as magma from the core of the planet moved toward the surface. He looked at Traun, at the face of the commander in deep concentration, sweat pouring from him as he used his mental powers to control the vast energy below him. Barnabus glanced nervously at the others. They too were concentrating, their combined psychic force now required to contain the great powers as they waited for it to maximise its potential.

Traun rose, his arms outstretched. Waiting, waiting. Only another moment, he thought, the energy seeming to consume him. The power was at its maximum. He visualised the enemy. The great globe of light, the ribbon of light moving upward, tapping the resources of the red sun, the resources that empowered Borgnoff in Its madness. Traun let his anger flow through him, directing the energy beneath him, focusing it, visualising for an instant the death which Borgnoff had inflicted on his fellow Atlanteans. His anger flew like a whip, and as it did so, he cried the command.

"Release!"

Instantly, Traun and his men relaxed their mental grip on the great power below them, giving it the opportunity to vent its pressure. For a moment, it subsided. But then, it found another route. The column of crystals had collapsed, leaving a great shaft, and the pressurised magma flowed into this. The force mounted, seeking release, moving upward.

It vented through the surface, held in a column by the field of gravity, gushing instantly through the space of the dome, moving now, a great serpent of living energy, through the outside atmosphere, directed by the vision which Traun held fast in his mind.

With the force of the planet's core, millions of tonnes of natural energy hit the ribbon of light only a few meters above the brightly glowing globe, the centre of Borgnoff's intelligence on the planet.

For a millisecond, the power of the magma matched the force of the ribbon. Borgnoff, taken by surprise, had little option. Had It the time, It could have increased the energy flow from the Red Giant, a force much greater than that which attacked It. But Borgnoff, too engrossed in Its fury at Jonathan, noticed the attack too late. Instantly, It withdrew, the energy which was Its intelligence moving back up the ribbon of light, back towards the Sun which harboured It. As it moved through the ribbon at close to the speed of light, the magma surmounted the energy which it faced. The umbilical cord tying the globe to the Red Giant glowed for a moment, then fractured. The released energy, a pinpoint of white-hot light, fed on the planet's oxygen, expanded for a moment, then exploded, levelling everything in its path.

As the Red Giant finally set, a sun born from the planet's centre shattered the twilight, washing a quarter of the hemisphere in its light.

The shock waves reached him as he fell, pushing him toward the wall of the globe. The white hot network of light came up to meet him, and for a moment he thought that he would be killed by the impact. But then, the faint tugs of the wind pulled at him, sucking him toward the centre.

Above him, the top of the globe shattered suddenly, a mixture of white-hot gasses and pieces of the structure falling toward him. He turned away, shielding himself from the light. The opening gaped in front of him, and then he was in it, darkness enveloping him. The wind here was hurricane-force, ripping at him, pulling him forward through a dark tunnel. He collided with the wall, and felt his shoulder pop, the pain darting through him. He clutched it, feeling the dried blood from Borgnoff's attack, his suit torn.

He thought that the tunnel was curving upward slightly, now parallel with the ground. Again and again, the gale bashed him against the tunnel's sides, pummelling him. He saw light in front of him; the wind slackened a bit. He put out his good arm, trying to touch the side, anything to stop his tumbling.

The light in front of him grew. An opening. He closed his eyes and started to pray. He was almost there. He opened his eyes, and as he did, he shot into daylight, falling again, fire all around him, falling, falling and then he hit, and felt water, cool and comforting, surrounding him, covering him. In his face and eyes. Into his mouth. Down his lungs . . . "This is just great," he thought, "I saved Cathy from the Borgnoff. And now we are both going to die from drowning instead!"

He didn't feel the hand reach out to grasp his hair, pulling him with steady strokes toward the far shore, as the temperature of the water rose rapidly. They laid him on the sand, and he heard footsteps and voices around him; gentle hands covering him, and lifting him. He opened his eyes for a moment, and thought he saw Cathy, a distant face looking at him, eyes full of concern. Then he lost consciousness again and did not hear her voice beside him or feel Barnabus touch the injured arm. Nor did he notice as the ragged survivors descended the steep cliff, lowering the makeshift stretcher in front of them or laying him on the rough transporter before they hurried him back through the bog, back to safety. They marched quickly in two groups; the girl and the teacher with the first, carrying the boy. The second group hauling the block of plate glass pieces, others carrying the fragments that they had found.

Now and then they stopped to rest, and the girl bent over him, brushing his hair from his eyes, caressing his cheek slightly. The teacher tut-tutted over the wounds and bruises and talked quietly to the leader. He shook his head slightly, smiling, and then they rose again.

With their load, it took them half the day to reach the monument, struggling through the boggy ground, the twin yellow suns now well over the horizon. At last, they were home, greeted by their people, and the older woman, her gown stained, her face shimmering, stood silently, a questioning look in her eyes. And when her Traun told her of all that had taken place, she crumpled to the ground, feeling the weight of timeless generations engulfing her, unconsoling. She was helped up by her people, and together they entered the monument, her head again held high. She fused the great door shut behind them, firm in her resolve to stand fast.

30

Jonathan opened his eyes, slowly, the bright light seeming to bounce off the back of his skull. He stared up, not seeing at first, then focused and saw Cathy. She leaned over him, her black hair falling on to his face, and she was smiling, tears on her cheeks. Tentatively, he put out a hand, feeling the wet on his fingers. She looked at him, crying, bending down, kissing him lightly. And then he had his good arm around her, holding her tightly, trying to ignore the pain that swept through him.

"Hey," he said gently. "What's that for?"

She laughed a little. "I don't know. I guess it's your reward."

He eased himself up slightly and she nestled against his good shoulder. "You mean I actually deserve a reward?"

She laughed again. "Well, maybe not. You certainly did screw things up there at the end."

"Ah, come on. I got you guys out, didn't I?"

"I guess so. But I'm not sure it was worth it. Landing in a lake is not my idea of fun. Still, I guess it beats landing on rock."

"I guess so." He tried to sit up straight, but pain shot through him. He gritted his teeth, gently pushing her off him.

"What's the matter?" she said, kneeling by him.

He grimaced. "Oh! I don't know. I hurt like hell, that's all."

"That's what you get when you try to pull off a rescue operation all by yourself."

"That's true," he said, reaching out to touch her hair. "But

I'm kind of glad I did."

She smiled again. "So am I."

He grinned. "Anyway, it's your fault. If you hadn't run away from that giant bug back in the woods, I wouldn't have had to bother."

"Stop complaining. We're alive, aren't we?"

He considered a moment. "Barely." He propped himself up on his good arm. "How's Psorsis, anyway?"

Cathy's smile faded. "You don't know, of course. He's dead."

"Christ," he muttered. "How's Kristiana taking it?"

She smiled briefly. "Stoically. When you're her age, I guess you've seen and felt most things."

"And Barnabus?"

"What about Barnabus?" Their teacher stood in the doorway, his overcoat burnt and torn, the right lens of his glasses shattered.

"What happened to you, Barnabus?"

"Nothing much, my boy. Just survived a few nuclear blasts. Now, if you two are done mooning at each other or whatever it is you're doing, I want you to come along with me. Kristiana needs us."

"Right." Painfully, Jonathan swung his feet to the floor. "Tell her the fighting Irish are on their way."

"Well put, my lad." Barnabus swung toward the door. "Coming?" Cathy and Jonathan moved as quickly as the boy could, in Barnabus's wake.

They walked briskly down the hallway, towards the place for their meeting with the visitors. Kristiana walked in front of Traun, her head bent slightly as her people moved back respectfully against the side of the granite walls. Since the loss of Psorsis, she had been subdued, her people giving her a wide berth as she grieved for him. She had not slept for three full days, choosing, instead, to monitor the situation outside.

She glanced towards her old lieutenant, a man who had shown more courage than sense, but who had still managed to help the younger people escape. Since the attack on Borgnoff, Traun had not bothered to change his uniform. It was torn and mud-streaked, a reminder of the battle. He, too, grieved for his younger master and to ease the pain did what he could to keep busy. He knew that the situation above the Atlantean stronghold was deteriorating rapidly. Since their attack, Borgnoff had moved out, away from the planet. Traun smiled wryly. It was a victory, of sorts. They had managed to force Borgnoff's hand for the first time in over five thousand years of conflict. He knew that in the next encounter victory was not remotely conceivable. Borgnoff simply had too much energy at Its disposal. If It wanted to, It could wipe out the entire planet with a single thought.

All they could hope for was a successful evacuation. Traun had discussed it at length with Kristiana. It seemed the only way out for their people – the only option for survival. They had but one problem. And that problem – at the moment – appeared insurmountable. In discussing it with Kristiana, it had become obvious to both of them that they still needed help from their visitors. They recognised the skills which these long-lost relatives brought to them. It remained to be seen, however, if these tools would be useful.

As he walked, he reflected on them. The young man, Jonathan, had proven himself in attempting to save Psorsis. The fact that he had failed was no reflection on his intent. Traun had heard the story of what he had done, and was frankly amazed that he now lived to tell the tale. He was definitely an asset to the Atlanteans in their struggle to survive.

His mind moved to Barnabus. While the old teacher had not exactly proven his usefulness, he had shown his bravery and loyalty to his charges. These traits were highly valued by Atlanteans and Traun could credit the older man with these now. He also knew of the mechanical skills of the scholar, and, while he could not understand them, hoped that they would prove to be useful, particularly in light of the urgent situation which they now faced.

The girl. Traun thought again about the girl, his feelings mixed. That she was also brave and loyal, he had no doubt. It was no fault of hers that the thing she faced was monstrous, overpowering. Yet Traun's mind wavered. The girl was different, somehow. She was efficient and powerful. Intelligent. There could be no doubt of that. In many ways, she reminded him of Kristiana. A younger version of his leader, a person whom he had never known, who had been born almost five thousand years before him. His mind paused, still revolving around Cathy, knowing that she was somehow significant to them, though not yet seeing how. Soon, he thought, soon, when they understand our predicament. Then, we shall see.

He walked quickly behind Kristiana, deep in thought. As he did, the ground shook slightly, the results of a renewed bombardment. Borgnoff had been relatively quiet since they had forced It back from Its nesting place. When the blast occurred, It had scurried up Its umbilical cord like a child returning to its mother's womb. It sat waiting – not that It was anything more than pure energy – cocooned in the nuclear warmth of the Red Giant, absorbing its energy, readying Itself. Now, however, It should have Its plan ready. Any day – even today, he thought – It could move against them. Forcing them to expose themselves. And that would spell disaster. As he moved down the passage with Kristiana, he thought about all of this, his mind focusing even more on the only option which seemed open to them: escape.

They met in the ante-chamber. The visitors on one side of the table, Kristiana and Traun on the other. It was different from previous meetings; the atmosphere was more relaxed, as if they understood each other now and could rely on one another.

Quickly, they brought Barnabus and the two students up to date on the situation. After ten minutes of discussion, Kristiana stopped talking. For a moment, the faint rumblings above them ceased. They sat quietly.

"So you see," Kristiana's low voice broke the silence,

"Borgnoff has complete control. The bombardments which we hear are merely a small taste of what is to come. As you know, Borgnoff has power which is beyond comparison. If It wanted to, It could simply dispose of this planet. One second here, the next gone." She passed her ancient hands quickly through the air, reminding Cathy of an executioner's blade. "However, It does not choose to be so quick about Its destruction."

"Why?" Barnabus sat, hands thrust deeply into his overcoat pockets. "What does It value that It has not already taken? Certainly, we have nothing to teach It. Nor, might I be so bold to say, do you."

Jonathan squirmed uncomfortably. "Don't forget the scrolls, Barnabus."

"Yes," Cathy whispered, "It wanted answers to the scrolls. That's why It killed Psorsis. It would have killed me, too, if Jonathan hadn't been around." She looked for a moment at Jonathan, her eyes softening. "I grant you, our lives are rather trivial compared to the power which that thing controls. It could have snuffed us out in a second and not been bothered in the least. But It wanted something more. Obviously, the knowledge which the scrolls possess must be incredibly powerful."

Kristiana turned slowly to Barnabus. "What she says is true. The scrolls can teach Borgnoff many things. While we might understand what my grandfather Psorsis gave to us, we do not yet have the mental faculties to practise it.

"As you know, Barnabus, we Altanteans long ago learned to control certain forces in nature. We can bend a certain number of these forces to our will, for the betterment of our species. Borgnoff, in many ways, does the same thing: transforming energy for Its own uses. Unfortunately," Kristiana frowned grimly, "those uses often bring about the demise of entire cultures. That said, It has certain limitations in this quest for ultimate power. The scrolls of Psorsis would remove those limitations. It would be able to call upon the total energy of the universe. In doing so, It would *become* the universe, spelling disaster for any living entity which It

232

considered a potential rival. Or unworthy to live in Its domain."

Cathy looked up. "That's why It took the scrolls. And why it was so important to get them back again."

"Yes," Traun replied. "We had to get them back, for two reasons. The first was to prevent Borgnoff from getting the knowledge which they possessed. The other reason was more immediate."

Barnabus sat, a frown on his face. "You needed the scrolls yourselves. You need them even now to protect you – and us, for that matter – from the forces of Borgnoff."

Kristiana nodded. "That's right. While we cannot yet apply, nor even understand, everything which my grandfather has written, we might yet learn at least enough to survive. To escape from the evil which we now face."

"That's fine, so what's the problem? I mean, the last I saw of the scrolls, they were falling down through that weird globe of lights." Jonathan turned to Traun. "You got me out, and Cathy. You found the remains of Psorsis. I have to take it that you got the scrolls, too."

Traun nodded. "Yes, we recovered them. It slowed down our evacuation, but we brought them home."

Jonathan looked back and forth between Traun and Kristiana. "Great. So that does it. You simply fit the scrolls into that incredible transport machine that you have up above, find some other planet, and transfer your people over. Isn't that what you were hoping to do? Isn't that why we went to rescue the things in the first place?"

Traun looked down at the table, silent. Kristiana sat upright, unwavering as ever. "Yes, that's right. That was the plan. It is what my son sacrificed himself for. But it cannot now happen as we had planned."

Barnabus sat straighter, expecting the worst. "Why, Kristiana? What has gone wrong?"

The old leader slumped forward slightly. "I will show you, Barnabus. Look. Look at what Borgnoff has done to the works of my grandfather."

Now, as Kristiana put out her hand, the stone wall of the chamber parted, revealing the scrolls. The scrolls for which so much had been lost; for which Psorsis had sacrificed himself.

The scrolls of Psorsis sat in a mound, wrecked beyond recognition. Intense heat had burnt them, fusing glass leaves to one another. In places, the glass had shattered leaving the manuscripts open to the elements, the ancient parchment decomposing quickly. Leaving nothing, not even a shadow. All in all, perhaps a third of the scrolls had been lost. Jonathan looked and understood. Borgnoff had tried to destroy them; he had seen It fire, trying to reach the scrolls as they fell beneath him. Unfortunately, the creature had been accurate. Too accurate. The beautiful symmetry was gone. The casing burnt. The contents ruined. It was too much even for Kristiana. As Cathy watched, great tears formed in the ancient eyes of the woman, streaming slowly down her cheeks. "They are gone." She muttered. "What is here now is useless. Fragments of their former wealth. Borgnoff has taken from us the heritage that was ours. Now, we have nothing. We can only wait."

Traun looked at Barnabus, then at Jonathan, finally at Cathy. "We have nothing. Now, we come to you. You were working on your electronic mechanism. Can you develop it in time to save us all?" Barnabus looked back, first at Kristiana, then at Traun, then over towards his students. The scrolls were in ruins. His hardware only half finished. He thought for a moment, and then slowly, their teacher smiled.

"Barnabus," Cathy said, "what are you thinking?"

"Oh, I don't know. Just an idea. Just an interesting idea."

Jonathan covered his face with his good hand. "Why do I get a bad feeling about this?"

Their teacher rose slowly, his eyes merry. "Come on, now. Stop complaining. Get up, and let's get to work." He turned to Kristiana, bowing slowly. "Madam, I would be delighted to help, if I can. We shall do our best. Simply our best! If I could have Traun and some of his men join me in the upper chamber in, say, twenty minutes?" Kristiana nodded her assent, her eyes flickering with interest and hope. "Many thanks,"

Barnabus replied. "Then, I'll be off about my business. Jonathan? Cathy?" he called to them. The trio left the chamber, Jonathan limping slightly, listening intently to their teacher as he described the plan which had come to mind.

31

"I don't know about this, Barnabus."

"Come now, Jonathan. We did it before. Certainly we can do it again."

Jonathan walked beside Barnabus, Cathy following close behind them. "What you're talking about just won't work. First of all, what you did back in Newgrange is nothing compared to what you have to do here. This is big stuff – mega!"

"I know that. But it's still feasible."

"It is not feasible. You don't know what you're getting us into. Why don't you just work on getting the three of us out of here?"

Cathy looked quickly at Jonathan, her eyes angry. "That's typical, Jonathan. Only thinking of yourself."

"Hey, come on! This is not our fight. I've been through enough. As far as I'm concerned, that Borgnoff thing, or whatever It is, can have this Godforsaken planet. I just want to go home."

"And leave these people behind us, Jonathan?" Barnabus shook his head slightly. "I don't think you mean that. Would you leave Kristiana? Or Traun? Or any of the Atlanteans? Would you leave them to be annihilated by this evil thing? I don't think so, Jonathan. You've sacrificed too much. You really did care about Psorsis. That's why you tried to rescue him. Can you just walk away now?"

Jonathan kept silent.

"It's all hypothetical, anyway." Cathy spoke up. "I'm

certain, Barnabus, that you haven't run any real calculations on what it might do to our solar system. I'm no astrophysicist, but you don't just throw a new planet into a sun system and expect the existing planets to keep on spinning around. Certainly, there has to be a reaction. The planetary gravitational fields will be disrupted. Orbits will change. It could be catastrophic." She looked at him, her dark eyes angry. "You could kill people."

Barnabus smiled. "I don't think so, Catherine. What we're going to do is to move the entire planet of Atlantis – the atmosphere, the people, everything – back to Earth's system. And, we're going to do it in such a way as to minimise any disturbances in the gravitational fields between the existing nine planets in the solar system."

Jonathan grimaced. "This I have to see. I don't mean to be disrespectful, Barnabus, but you're going to kill everybody doing this. The people left here, the people on Earth, everybody. Anyway, how are you going to move an entire planet? This monument's transporter unit is out. The scrolls destroyed. Remember?"

Barnabus quickened his pace, slightly, moving up the stairway that took them into the top chamber of the monument. "Oh, I remember. We're just going to have to fix it, that's all."

"Oh! Is that all!"

Barnabus started to run up the stairs, his shattered glasses bouncing on top of his nose. "Would you both please hurry? If we're to do anything, we must be quick. We don't have much time. I remind you that the other option is to do nothing. To wait until Borgnoff comes and destroys us all."

Jonathan looked up at him, trying to ignore the pain in his shoulder as he walked up the stairs. "OK. I see your point. We don't have many options."

Barnabus stopped, turning to face him. "None."

Jonathan looked at Cathy. "I guess I'm in, if you're in."

"I don't think we have a choice," she said.

He looked up at his teacher. "Right. So what do you want us to do?"

Barnabus smiled broadly. "You'll see, Jonathan. You'll see."

The entity had searched for many years. Its vast intelligence had focused on the small, outlying planet in the spiral galaxy, noting the crystal blues of the oceans and oxygenated atmosphere, and knew that here the miracle of life had also begun. It sensed, however, that it had been too late. The evil had already arrived leaving a wake of destruction in its path. Still, it had not finished its genocide. Here and there, pockets of humanity laboured to restore what had been destroyed.

For a moment, the facet which was of naKuna dwelled above this planet, attempting to correct that which had been mutilated. To the survivors of the holocaust, it provided gentle winters and warm summers. And it was pleased as it saw the life forms prosper once again. For many years in human time, the representative of naKuna comforted and nurtured the survivors of Earth. And in that time, as it comforted, it waited.

Then, one day, it felt the far-off cataclysm, the cries of despair that foretold the death of life. From its orbit, it gazed at the humans who now moved freely over their planet, and blessed them, knowing that the future was now in their hands. They would live or perish as they chose. Then it moved away from the system of nine planets, searching for the source of the signal, focusing on it; now accelerating away from the bright spiral galaxy, pummelling the universe around it with energy. Transmuting it. Simplifying it. The universe is a vast ocean. And while naKuna had long ago discovered what humans would call Einstein's theory of relativity, they had also noted other laws of physics which humankind had only glimpsed. As it maximised the local energy, so too did its gravitational field grow stronger. Strong enough, finally, to bend space around it, skipping now as lightly as a stone upon a pond, skipping from one point on the curve to the next . . . towards a meeting with its brother.

The monument was in much worse shape than it had been before. While Borgnoff had not yet mounted a concerted attack, It had periodically sent a small reminder towards it, the red-hot fingers of heat bolting from a mottled cloudscape.

Kristiana had tried to protect it by mounting a defence shield. The shield, powered by the internal energy of the planet, was strong enough to ward off most of the attack. Now and again, however, the attacking energy was too strong, and the defence would drop momentarily. When the energy struck, it blasted hundreds of kilos of earth from the top of the monument. Inside, the roof structure had started to crack, the great walls of the chamber pummelled by forces which it could not possibly match.

Jonathan walked across the floor of the chamber, stepping through rubble that had dropped from the ceiling. "If that Borgnoff thing launches a real attack, this monument is history."

Barnabus nodded. "That's why we have to work fast." He walked up to the dais. The huge altar of quartz was silent, the smaller chamber within it gutted and the scrolls which belonged there not yet replaced, perhaps never to be replaced.

Cathy stood next to her teacher. "OK, now what, Barnabus? I mean, we have the scrolls, but they're half-destroyed. So there's no power."

He smiled. "No power yet, Cathy."

She put her hands on her hips. "Look, I know that you created a power unit for the dais at Newgrange. But this is different, Barnabus. You don't have all your tools. Nor enough parts, for that matter. You said so yourself."

"That's right." Jonathan walked toward him. "You lost half your stuff in that swamp, don't you remember?"

"And the power you're talking about – power to transport an entire planet – has to be tremendous. You can't just put together something like that."

Barnabus looked at them. "Just remember something. Remember what the scrolls did in this monument. What my machine did in Newgrange. It focused the energy from below the monument through the user. Enabling him to reach out with his mind. Grabbing that energy. Shaping it to the user's will. The scrolls, or indeed, my machine, only helps the user to access the energy. It does not provide the energy. The planet does that. Nor did the scrolls direct the energy. The user did that. Again, the scrolls only provided access. And that access was limited. Certainly, Newgrange and this monument just tapped into the energy available in a localised area. Now, I ask you," Barnabus thrust his hands into his pockets, removing some notes. "What would happen if we tapped all the planet's energy? Certainly, with more power available, we should be able to do more. Move more people, maybe even a building . . . "

"Or an entire planet," Cathy whispered.

Barnabus talked as if he were back in school, standing at the blackboard. "That's right, Cathy! Or an entire planet!"

"I don't know about this," Jonathan muttered.

"Ah, Traun! Delighted that you could make it." Jonathan turned as the old commandant walked into the chamber.

"You asked for me?"

"Precisely!" Barnabus said. "Just the man! I was hoping that you could join us." He looked at Traun, smiling. "I was just wondering, would it be possible to have the scrolls moved?"

The old warrior, still dazed from battle, looked at Barnabus suspiciously. "What would you want with the scrolls, teacher?"

"Oh, not much, Traun. Not much. Just an idea that I have. Jonathan? Cathy? Come over here." Barnabus stood, his arm on Traun's shoulder, his voice raised in excitement.

When he was finished, he looked at the small group. "Now, how does that sound?"

Cathy and Traun remained silent. Only Jonathan spoke. "I told you that I wasn't going to like this."

What was left of the scrolls was pulled into the chamber. Barnabus was amazed at the damage. He walked around the scrolls, examining them. "Right," he said finally. "Let's get started. Cathy, why don't we begin to take them apart?"

Jonathan looked at him quizzically. "You don't really expect to get into that mess, do you?"

"Certainly! Other than the fact that we need to try to realign the glass plates, I want to get my hands on those manuscripts.

From what Kristiana has indicated, her grandfather was a mathematics wizard. I'm hoping to get some hints on energy output from them." He turned to Traun. "Kristiana is coming up here, I hope?"

Traun nodded. "She will be here soon."

"Good! She knows more about the contents of the scrolls than anyone else alive. Mind you, she's had thousands of years to study them." He turned to Jonathan. "Now, Jonathan. You know what you have to do?" The teacher was serious, his hands deep in his pockets. Jonathan stared back at him, his face sceptical.

"Sure. Just go back out there and get that briefcase full of trash that you left in the river. No problem, let me tell you."

"It's not trash, Jonathan," Cathy said softly. "You know that Barnabus needs those electrical components."

"You'd think that in a place like this, we could just send down to the local electrical shop." He looked at Traun disparagingly. "Some civilisation you have here."

The soldier looked over at him. "We never had the need to develop physical electromagnetic capabilities. Our control of planetary power was always enough."

"Yeah, yeah. Well, this time it's *not* enough, is it?"

"Gentlemen!" Barnabus glowered at Jonathan. "Are we going to stand around arguing or are we going to work?"

Jonathan sniffed. "To work, I guess. I'm just not looking forward to going out there right now."

Traun spoke. "It's quiet at the moment. Borgnoff is not active."

The student shook his head. "When that thing isn't doing anything, it just means that It's getting ready to do something. And I don't particularly feel like being in Its sight when It does it!" He sighed. "Well, if we're going to go, let's get going."

Cathy walked close to him. She reached up, kissing him on the cheek. "Be careful."

Jonathan looked at her intently. "I don't intend to become a corpse. Nor do I intend to get sucked into that giant pink vacuum back there in the stream. You just stay here and help Barnabus. I'll be all right." Finally, he turned to Traun. "You coming, Commander?"

The two walked out of the chamber. Cathy reached for Barnabus, tears in her eyes as she watched Jonathan leave the chamber.

32

Traun and Jonathan crouched at the side of the stream, the same stream which Jonathan, Cathy and Barnabus had waded through when they first came to Atlantis. Jonathan looked down into the muck riding on the surface. The reddish-green gunk still lay congealed on top of the water. Now and then, a giant bubble of gas broke the surface, spraying the two with bits of red matter and brown mud.

"This still smells like a sewer."

Traun looked at him, the old man's craggy face cracking a slight smile. "Surely this is not as unpleasant as Borgnoff's dome?"

Jonathan considered. "I don't know. At least the dome didn't smell." Slowly he lowered his arm into the water, trying to find the bag that he knew lay under the surface somewhere. As he did, Traun scanned the horizon. The sky was clear, quiet. In the distance, the ruins of the old capital stretched before him. Millions of people had already died. Now his people were threatened with extinction. He looked then at the boy, knowing that their survival depended on what these descendants of his people could invent. He shook his head. He suddenly felt his age.

Jonathan withdrew his arm suddenly, breaking Traun's train of thought. "I can't find it. It's down there somewhere."

"What is it, exactly, that we're looking for?"

"A briefcase. A brown briefcase, to be precise. Loaded with electrical parts. God only knows what this watery crap has done to them."

Traun was puzzled. "A briefcase?"

"Yeah. Like a box with a carrying handle. We use it to pack things into when we're travelling. Barnabus had loaded it with electrical gear. Diodes. Microswitches. That sort of thing." Traun's face was blank, uncomprehending. "Never mind," Jonathan sighed. "It's in here, anyway. We dropped it in when we first arrived. I tried to get to it, but this huge pink snaky thing went for it first. Never saw anything like it." He reached into the water again. "Mind you, I don't think it found the case appetising, so it must be in here somewhere"

"A pink thing, you say?" Traun smiled slightly. "Ah. You mean the rantor. Yes. They live in this water. They eat the waste materials. They recycle our waste matter."

Jonathan looked down into the muck again, his face a scowl. "You mean this really *is* a sewer?" He looked at Traun. "The things I've had to put up with on this trip." He stood up, lost in thought for a moment. "Well, I guess there's only one thing to do. But I sure don't feel like doing it."

Gradually, Jonathan stepped into the slime, his hands below the surface, feeling for the briefcase.

Traun stayed at the side of the water, scanning the surface. "Be careful, Jonathan," he said.

Jonathan turned to him. "What do you mean, be careful?"

"Ah. Well, sometimes the rantor has trouble discerning the difference between human waste matter and real humans. For this reason, it's always been our policy to prohibit children from coming near this area."

Jonathan looked into the water and sighed. "I know. I had a little run-in with the pink slime once already. Wait until I get my hands on Barnabus."

"But no matter, Jonathan." Traun stood on the bank, his target sights planted on the surface of the water. "If I see it, I will do my best to kill it."

"Fine. Just make sure that you hit that thing and not me."

He searched the water again. His shoulder began to hurt, and he longed for his bed. He still wore his suit of flexible armour, and this gave him some warmth in the muck. And a weapon. Now and then, he looked up, focusing the whorl sights on the surface. The water remained quiet.

He heard a splash to his right. "What was that?"

Traun looked at him. "What?"

"Over there." Jonathan pointed. "Come on, didn't you see anything?"

"No, nothing."

"Right. Well, keep looking, would you?"

Jonathan walked forward. He stepped on something. "Here. I think I found it!" Carefully, he kicked at the thing below him, moving it slightly. "That feels right. Now, if I can only get to it." He moved his hands lower. His chin was just above the slime. Slowly, slowly. Almost there. Just about there. He felt the sides of the case, trying to grasp it. "God, it's slippery."

"There!" Traun shouted hoarsely from behind. Instantly, Jonathan was blinded by Traun's weapon, as it released its power. The water boiled three feet in front of him, steam soaring into the air. Jonathan spun around. "What? Where is it?"

Traun pointed. "In front of you!" Jonathan looked. Nothing. "Great. Look, I've almost got the case. Keep that pink thing off me, will you?"

"In the name of Psorsis!" He heard Traun, and looked up. The clear sky was filling with cloud, angry bolts of lightning hurtling from the black columns of moisture. Behind them, Jonathan could make out a glow – the red furnaces of hell itself.

"What is that? Let's get out of here."

He reached down again, finally grasping the case. He pulled, but it wouldn't budge. Then he felt the pressure on his forearm. It had him firmly in its cylindrical jaw, dragging him under. He fought wildly in the brackish water. He couldn't see the thing that had him, only feel it. It pulled at him, trying to tear his arm from its socket. He rolled, attempting to loosen the grip. It was no use. He fought, his wounded shoulder aching, trying to move up. Losing power. He felt his lungs ache, and wanted to breath. Oxygen. I need air.

Suddenly he was above the surface, thrown into the air, and he saw it. He screamed. Both for intake of oxygen and in the terror of what he saw. This time, it was huge. It had no eyes, only mouths. Five of them. One was attached to his arm. The other four writhed, gaping holes attached to metre long stalks, water pouring from their gaping openings. Hundreds of cilia surrounded each mouth opening, ugly, moving, the stalks wavering towards Jonathan, searching to gain a hold on his flailing legs and arms.

"Traun! For God's sake, shoot the thing!"

"Steady, now, boy! Hold on!"

He felt the beast rotating, and now his head was pointed toward the surface again. The mouth moved down, dumping him again into the water. It thrashed about, pummelling his body against the muddy bottom, forcing water in through his mouth. He tried to move, to flail out, to force himself out from under it. He needed to breathe. Needed to breathe right now. This wasn't fair. Not after everything else. Not after the trip here. The show-down with Borgnoff. Not after Cathy.

He felt, more than heard, the squeal from above him. The thing relaxed its grip suddenly. He moved a little, feeling the mushy jaws drop free from his arm and moved up, trying to find the surface. He was disoriented, not knowing which way was up, which way to the surface – to air. His arms went numb, and he knew that he wouldn't make it. Then a seering pain ripped through his body as he felt his arm grabbed, his neck snapped back, an agonising explosion in his wounded shoulder. He was pulled up, seeing the surface of red, his breath coming in painful spasms, shooting through his lungs.

Traun hauled him through the slime, dumping him unceremoniously onto the muddy bank. Jonathan lay stunned for a moment, then his head cleared. He looked up at Traun. "Great to know that you can shoot with that thing."

Traun looked down on the boy. "I was lucky, I think."

Jonathan gazed out over the water. The rantor lay on its side, steam spilling up from the wound in its pink tubular body, two of the mouths still writhing. Slowly, he got to his knees. Traun was back in the water, the green algae floating around his belly. He reached down and brought up the briefcase, dripping with mud. "This, I take it, is what we came for?"

"That's it all right."

"Good. Then I suggest that we get back to the monument. I believe that we can expect another visit from Borgnoff quite soon. Look." Traun pointed toward the heavens.

The running battle with the five-headed vacuum cleaner had made Jonathan forget. Now he remembered and looked quickly to the sky. The clouds were black, threatening, throwing off great bolts of energy. They glowed eerily, lit from behind, casting an ugly red light on to the remnants of the city. As Jonathan watched, the clouds began to spin in a great circle, as if caught in the currents of a huge whirlpool. Then, at the centre, they split suddenly, bright red light pouring down on them, turning the planet into a hellish playground. Jonathan held his hands up to his eyes. He tried to see beyond the clouds, to determine what caused the light. He saw It, and slowly lowered his hand. "Something tells me Borgnoff is in business again. Maybe we should get back."

Traun glanced at him. "A wise suggestion, I think." He helped Jonathan up. They looked again at the great swirling pattern of cloud, the huge red eye at Its epicentre. Then, they ran for the cover of the monument.

33

The doors opened. The doors closed. The group turned to look at them.

"What happened to you?" Cathy ran to him, supporting him around the waist.

"Don't worry about me. I'll tell you later. You won't believe me anyway." He turned, looking at the group coming towards him. He saw Kristiana first, then his teacher.

"Barnabus. Here's your materials. I hope it was worth it." Traun dropped the dripping case onto the ground.

Jonathan looked at his teacher. "I hope you have this stuff wrapped up well. It's been sitting at the bottom of that muck for days. And you wouldn't believe the company it's had."

Barnabus scurried over, picking up the case, holding it to its chest. "Well done, Jonathan, Traun. We're just about ready for them, I think."

"Good. Have you thought of looking outside?" Kristiana had entered the chamber and now she walked over to him. Jonathan looked at her and thought she looked magnificent. She had put the death of her son behind her and stood, the white wool of her gown radiant.

Not bad, for her age, he thought. "Yes, we know. Borgnoff is attacking. It didn't look like It was going to throw a little bit of lightning our way this time. No. I think It really means business."

Kristiana stared at him blankly. "Yes. As you say, It means business. For over five thousand years It has meant business, and for that long, the people of Atlantis have managed to survive. Hundreds of civilisations have faced Its threat. We watched as It destroyed other planets within our system, watched, powerlessly, as It wiped hundreds of civilisations from the face of the universe. It is relentless. Always craving power. Always demanding more. Always killing! It has taken my son, millions of my people. It tried to steal the very knowledge which we depend upon, the scrolls of Psorsis! And still, It demands more."

She stood erect, power surging through her, her face shimmering in its glow as she called on the forces of the planet for support. She turned, facing Barnabus. "How quickly will you be ready?"

He shook his head. "I don't know. An hour. Maybe two."

"It will be too late. If Borgnoff is not stopped, It will destroy the little that remains of my people. Then the lives of Psorsis, of Midreas – of all my ancestors – will have been in vain."

She glanced at Traun. "Where are the rest of our people?"

"The remaining survivors are sheltered within the monument, Kristiana."

"Good. Barnabus, you make your preparations. In the meantime, I have other work to do. Traun, stay with these people. Help them. Do not be concerned about me." She strode from the chamber, Traun watched her, and knew that he was probably seeing the last of his leader.

The chamber floor shook from the impact of the attacks above them. Since Kristiana had left, the quiet which they had enjoyed had been replaced by a constant bombardment. Borgnoff had obviously finished Its preparations and was letting loose a torrent of destructive energy upon the planet. The monument seemed to be Its primary target.

Traun ran to the front entrance of the great mound, pulling the gold portal open. What he saw made him freeze, fear coursing through him. He closed the door, sealing it behind him. He made his way back to the visitors, who were busy working on the floor of the chamber.

"I hope that you are nearly ready, Barnabus."

The teacher looked up from a pile of spare parts. He had spent the past hour disentangling the mess and checking the pieces for water damage. Most of the components had survived. He was, however, concerned about some of the small microprocessing units. Fortunately, he had thought to pack a dozen of these. They had been pre-programmed back in his workshop. He puzzled through them, hoping that the programme for the Newgrange dais would work for this much larger structure.

He turned to Traun, absently studying a circuit board. His notes, long hidden in the pockets of his torn coat, lay in front of him, the electrical diagrams and mathematical calculations providing him with the basic outlines of his design.

"What? What did you say, Traun?"

"Borgnoff. It is coming now."

"What?" Jonathan walked over from the dais, Cathy behind him. They had been pulling apart the scrolls, page by page, searching for a specific series of mathematical calculations which Barnabus had given to them. Now, the glass-covered pages of the scrolls, many shattered or partly melted, lay scattered on the floor, the glass housing still half full. "What do you mean, 'It's coming now?'"

Traun stood at full attention, a commander under attack, but with no troops to lead.

"As I said," he stated stiffly. "We are about to be attacked. If you would care to confirm this for yourself, you are welcome to look."

Jonathan moved to the door, Cathy at his shoulder. "You know, Cathy," he said as he walked, "sometimes I don't know why we listen to this guy. I mean, this Borgnoff thing may be a nasty piece of business, but we're inside, we're getting ready to leave this blister of a planet, so what's the problem?" Jonathan pulled the door open, and glanced outside. "You see what I mean? What's there to worry about?"

Cathy stood on tiptoe, looking over his shoulder. "Maybe we should worry about that, Jonathan," she said, pointing.

He looked, and slammed the door shut. He ran back to Barnabus. "Barnabus! How long before we're ready to leave this crazy place?"

The teacher had settled in behind his pile of electronic gear, his battery-powered soldering iron in his hand. "Sorry? You were saying, Jonathan?"

"Barnabus! We've got to get out of here! You should see what's outside."

"And what, may I ask, is outside?"

Traun bent down slightly, face to face with the old teacher. "Borgnoff, I'm afraid."

"Ah. It's coming at last, is It?"

"Yes," Traun replied.

"Come on, Traun! Tell him what's really coming!" He knelt down, grasping Barnabus by the shoulder. "I don't know how, Barnabus, but Borgnoff is moving that entire Red Giant towards us."

Barnabus rose, holding his soldering iron in mid-air. "What!"

Cathy looked at him, her face distorted with fear. "He's right, Barnabus. Somehow, Borgnoff has taken control of the Red Giant. It's moving in on the planet. You should feel it outside. The temperature must have gone up by fifty degrees already."

Their teacher stared at them grimly. "Yes. There is some sense in that. Borgnoff has always used stellar objects as methods of destruction. We know that It has used comets to destroy planets. It would also have the power to control the movement of an entire sun." He thought for a moment longer. "Since we can do nothing about it, I suggest that we keep on working."

"But Barnabus! Any minute now we're going to be killed!"

Barnabus glared at Jonathan for a moment, then relaxed, letting a smile come to his face, the salt-and-pepper moustache shaking for a moment as the man chuckled slightly. "And what would you have us do, Jonathan? Throw rocks at it?" He shook his head. "No, we will never defeat It. Our only hope is escape. And the only way to do that is to keep on working. Now, have you found those calculations yet?"

Cathy shook her head. "No, not yet."

Barnabus's mouth tightened. "Well, I'm afraid you'll have to find them. I had a word with Kristiana. Those calculations are necessary if we're going to tap the power resources which we'll need to escape Borgnoff. Now, get back to work and find them." He settled down again behind his hardware. "I'll start to assemble what I can, and, Traun, what do you intend to do?"

The commander smiled a little, and then knew what he had to do. "I have already checked on our people. They are confined to their quarters, and I have told them that you are working on our escape. That is all I can do. Now, I will go to find Kristiana. She gave me orders to stay here to help you. But as far as I can see, you don't need my help, whereas Kristiana might."

Barnabus looked up at the old warrior. "That's fine, Traun. You have given us more than enough help. Go find Kristiana."

Traun walked to the door, pausing to look back at the visitors. "I cannot say that I have particularly enjoyed your visit here. You all – you in particular, Jonathan – have given me nothing but trouble." Traun smiled slightly. "That said, I wish you luck."

"And to you, Traun." The commander pulled open the door, and for a moment the intense light of the Red Giant filled the gloom of the chamber. Then the door closed, and Traun was gone to find his leader.

34

Traun struggled through the devastated countryside, making his way toward the remnants of the city. As he walked, he looked up above him. The whorling mass of clouds had cleared slightly. Now, the sky was filled by the huge spectre of the Red Giant. He guessed that its apparent size had grown over fifty times. It was moving toward the planet at an incredible speed and Traun knew that Borgnoff would snuff out the life of what was left of his civilisation in an instant. Even now, he knew that ultraviolet light and alpha particles were pummelling the planet, the atmosphere no longer dense enough to shield them from the deadly attack. It meant the end of over five thousand years of civilisation and he felt anger grow in him. It might be the end of everything that he knew but Traun would not simply stand by and let the beast destroy them without a fight.

He shielded his eyes, looking up at the inferno which moved in on them. The Red Giant had changed slightly. He looked, and saw that its round shape had been altered, distended, was elliptical now rather than globular. Inside the raging nuclear furnace, the intelligence that was Borgnoff existed, fuelled by the energy of the great red sun. Behind him, the two yellow suns had also risen over the horizon. Traun stood, his armour-shielded figure casting three shadows, and wished that he had the strength of three men. But even then, he knew that it would not be enough.

He walked on, searching for her in the rubble. He knew that

Kristiana would be hiding, biding her time. Somehow, she intended to stall the force that would fall upon them. Giving the visitors time until they completed their machine, until they could play their last gambit. If it didn't work, the dreams of many lifetimes would be smashed into a billion atoms, a smear of dust and gas floating in an empty corner of the universe.

The earthquake struck suddenly. Traun staggered awkwardly, trying to keep his balance. The ground rolled and tore and he moved with it, keeping his feet like a sailor on the deck of a ship in rough weather. He knew instantly what had happened. The movement of the Red Giant had changed the gravitational equilibrium of the planet. The reactive nature of physics meant that the planet of Atlantis had to compensate. Now it was falling into the path of the sun, its speed increasing as the gravitational pull increased. He knew that they had only minutes before the planet came apart, splitting, rocketing into the fire that approached it.

He saw her then. Kristiana stood on a small knoll, her robe whipped by the wind, her regal face disdainfully unafraid of what approached. Traun ran, stumbling, skirting the shattered remnants of what used to be his planet's capital. Now, he was with her, standing at her side, the old warrior once again aiding his leader.

She looked at him, a faint smile moving over the ancient face, her body shimmering with its final summoning of power. "As I remember, Traun, I had asked you to stay with our visitors."

He shrugged, his haggard face solemn. "They function best on their own."

Her eyes lighted with momentary laughter. She knew his loyalty well. "Ah. So then you decided to find me."

"Yes." He stared at her, his face expressionless. "I thought that I should make myself useful."

She nodded. "I understand. How do the visitors progress?"

He shook his head. "The work goes slowly. The teacher, Barnabus, believes that he can make the machine work. But he needs time."

She nodded slowly. "So I thought." She looked at the thing above them, the shimmering power about her body reflecting the Red Giant's angry glow. "Unfortunately, it will take them more time than Borgnoff chooses to give us."

Traun remained silent, waiting. Kristiana sighed gently. "I have enjoyed living, Traun. I have been given great satisfaction by what we have been able to achieve. And I have become angry at what has happened to us. Thousands of years of work have been annihilated. My son killed. And for what reason?" She turned to him, and he saw tears glistening in her eyes. "For no reason! Only to satisfy the ego of Borgnoff!" She looked toward the heavens, into the raging furnace that was to be their destruction. "Ah, but yet we may flee. Yet we might outwit this adversary that has been our undoing for so many years. We may not yet be able to destroy It, but at least we can flee from It so that future generations might yet survive."

Kristiana placed her hand on Traun's shoulders. "Will you follow yet one more order, my friend?"

He smiled fiercely, expectantly. "When have I ever disobeyed your orders, Kristiana?"

The woman laughed harshly. "Never. Well, then, let us together give our visitors the time they need to save our people. Now, Traun. Here is what you must do. Think with me. Think of the planet, of its energy, its magnificence. Think of the great rivers which flow below us, of the fields of energy which surround us, of the great core of power which is buried far beneath us. Focus on these things, Traun, and join your thoughts with mine."

Traun closed his eyes, concentrating as he was told. And as he did so, he felt the ancient powers flow up through him, surrounding him, joining every fibre of his being with those of the leader that he had served for a lifetime.

Its senses felt the power and fear, and it released the energy, decelerating, allowing space-time to move back into four dimensions. And before it burned a system of three suns painted against the blackness of the universe. In the billionth of a second, it understood what it sensed. Three of the planets in the small system were already laid to waste. The red sun, moving now against all known laws, hovered over a small, fragrant globe which swarmed with life.

Enmity stirred in the heart of naKuna. It moved not only to protect, but also to punish.

35

"For God's sake, close the door and get over here to help!" Jonathan was standing by the great door of the monument, his body bathed in red light, staring mesmerised as the wrath of Borgnoff descended on the planet. Cathy and Barnabus were poring over the glass plates of the scrolls.

"Jonathan! Come on!" Cathy cried. "If we don't find this formula, you can forget about ever getting back home."

"I'm coming!" Jonathan tore himself away from the door, running back into the centre of the great room. "Hey, I don't want to get anyone frightened or anything, but if we're going to do something, we'd better get to it. That Borgnoff thing is getting closer."

Barnabus looked up from where he had been studying the scrolls. He smiled stiffly. "Jonathan, if you don't get down here and help us, I'm going to feed you to Borgnoff, personally!"

"Gotcha!" Jonathan got down on his knees. Dozens of glass plates were spread out over the stone floor. Each plate was covered with hundreds of lines of mathematical symbols, the great thoughts of a man whose brain had long turned to dust. "What are we looking for?"

"Here! We're looking for something like this." Barnabus scrawled a series of symbols on some spare paper. "See? Five parallel lines, then this symbol here, see? This circle surrounded by a square. Then this series of waves."

"What does it mean?"

Barnabus glanced up at him for a moment. "Well, to be honest, I'm not sure yet."

"Terrific." Jonathan glanced at the mass of electrical equipment that Barnabus had been working on. It didn't look like much. Just a hodge-podge of circuit boards, transistors, and wire harnesses slung together in no apparent order. A series of microprocessors lay to the side; the laptop computer stood ready near them. "And that junk over there," he pointed, "you're expecting that to get us out of here?"

The old teacher stood stiffly. "Yes, I do. With the right mathematical formulas, I'll be able to programme the microprocessors correctly. I'll then attach the hardware – 'that junk,' as you so delicately call it – to the scrolls. The scrolls will provide the primary focus. But my hardware will be able to control the power source more accurately. And more importantly, I'll be able to draw energy from further afield."

"Enough to move a planet?"

Barnabus stared at the student. "Let us all hope so."

Cathy stood glaring at him, hands on hips. "We're not going to get anywhere, Jonathan, if we just sit around here and talk about it."

Jonathan glanced at her. "All right. I'll start helping. But this is crazy, if you ask me."

"Nobody's asking you. Now help us find those symbols!" Cathy bent down again, studying the scrolls intently.

The earthquake hit suddenly. One minute, the three were on their hands and knees. The next, the chamber was rolling; small chunks of rock falling from the ceiling, forty feet above them, smashing the plates that lay exposed on the floor. Jonathan covered his head, rolling tightly into a ball. He felt himself being picked up and thrown against the side of the dais, his injured shoulder taking the full force of the blow. He lay for a moment, the pain going in and out of his body, waiting for the ground to stop moving. "I wish we could get out of this place." He rolled over on to his hands and knees, holding his shoulder. "I don't know about you, Barnabus, but I'm getting tired of this planet of Atlantis."

Barnabus and Cathy stood up. "Are you all right?"

"Oh, sure." Jonathan held himself rigid, trying to focus on

the ground in front of him. "I take it that little jolt means we're running out of time."

Barnabus glanced at them glumly. "I'd say you're correct."

"Well, if we've about had it, I'd like to go on record as saying that I've had a pretty lousy time, Barnabus." He looked around at his teacher. "Some trip! I didn't mind the mud so much. Or being shot at by lightning bolts. Or . . . " he glanced up at the chamber ceiling, " . . . being stuck in this quasi-megalithic monstrosity. I didn't even mind wrestling with some overgrown alien garbage disposal. But what I hated, Barnabus, what I really hated, was having to face this Borgnoff thing. Getting whacked in the shoulder was bad enough. I really didn't need to come up against that moron."

Cathy moved over to him, kneeling down beside him, her arm around his good shoulder. "Come on, Jonathan, it wasn't *that* bad."

"Hah! What do you know about it? You spent most of your time hanging in mid-air. *I* was the one that had to try to reason with that thing. At least we beat It . . . that time." He sighed wistfully. "And now, It's going to win. After all we've been through!"

She squeezed his arm gently. "We could beat It yet."

He shook his head. "I don't think so. It's going to be here any second. I just want to get home. It would have been nice to make it home, wouldn't it?" He looked at her, laughing ruefully. "The other kids never would have believed it."

Cathy shook her head, smiling slightly. "No, they wouldn't have."

He turned his face, looking into her eyes. "And if we had made it home, I would have finally been able to ask you out."

"Well who says that I would have gone out with you?"

Jonathan smiled. "I think you would have."

Cathy returned his smile. "Yes. I'd go out with you, Jonathan."

Jonathan laughed again, shaking his head. "Great. Here I am, who knows how many millions of miles from home, waiting to be instantly obliterated, and I finally get you to go out with me."

"If you'd stop feeling sorry for yourself, we might still have a chance."

"Well . . . maybe." He shook his head again, trying to get his eyes to focus. "All we need to do is find those damn mathematics equations, I take it."

She nodded. "That's right. If we had those, we could do something! We could get this crazy transport system to work again! We'd save ourselves! Save this world!"

He rested for a moment more. He looked up at her again. "OK, if you say so. Help me up." Jonathan looked down at the floor. He was kneeling on one of the glass plates, its surface shattered, Psorsis's calculations barely visible through the opaque glass. He looked at them, then he looked up at Cathy. "Didn't you say you were looking for a circle in a box? And a series of waves?"

She nodded. "That's right. And five parallel lines."

He pointed. "You mean like those?"

She looked. "Barnabus! Quick, over here!"

Barnabus peered up. "What?"

"He's found them! Come on!"

The teacher made his way quickly across the rubble. Cathy helped Jonathan crawl away from the plate. Then Cathy and her teacher swept the pieces of broken glass and dust away, exposing the ancient manuscript.

"Great God! Look at this!" Barnabus swept his fingers over the series of equations. "See here? Look at the interrelationships."

Cathy studied them intently. "But they're not Roman numerals."

"That's of no consequence. See? Look here." He pointed again. "Note the repetition. Now, move down here to this equation." He pointed down the page. "See? The equation repeats itself every three lines."

She shook her head, not understanding. "I don't follow you, Barnabus."

He put his hands into his coat pockets, pensive. "We must try to put ourselves into Psorsis's shoes . . . or sandals as the case may be. Kristiana stated that these equations had something to do with the control of forces." ⚫

Cathy thought for a moment. "You mean like vectors?"

He stared at her. "My God, child. That's it! Vectors! These lines and squiggles are vectors! Think back to our discussions on vector analysis. The material we went through in class. That's it! Look! Here and here . . . and here again!" He pointed excitedly at the equations. "Psorsis is explaining that we can use thought control to vector a variety of power sources into one gigantic focal point. A focal point that we can manipulate! That can be used to control space, time, physical objects! By applying our thought processes properly – and through the use of a little electronic wizardry – we just might be able to pull this off. Here! Help me with this!"

Barnabus bent over, gently picking the manuscript up off the floor, trying to avoid breaking the glass housing further. "Bring it over here to the laptop."

Jonathan watched them. "Hey, I don't mean to be the bearer of bad tidings or anything, but aren't we running out of time?"

"No, no. We're fine. Ten more minutes. Fifteen, perhaps! That's all we need!"

Jonathan limped towards the door of the monument. He opened it, looking out. "I don't know. You might want to come here and look at this, Barnabus."

"In a minute, Jonathan!"

"I'm telling you, you should see this."

"All right, all right!" Barnabus moved to him quickly, Cathy following. "Now what was it that you wanted to show me?"

Jonathan pointed, shielding the glare of the Red Giant with his hands. "I don't know what you think, but I think we're out of time."

Barnabus looked. Above them, the great nuclear furnace of the Red Giant filled the sky, its interior alive with pinpoints of fire, a universal hell that would consume them. And in the exact centre of the sun, staring at the world of Atlantis, the great eye of Borgnoff looked out, contemplating the destruction of Its foe.

36

Kristiana felt the old power enter her, coursing through her, surging through her entire being. She concentrated, reaching down with her thoughts, down into the planet that was Atlantis. As she did so, she remembered Earth, fertile Earth that she had left so many generations ago. She had left because of the terror that had plagued her and her people, the people of Psorsis and Midreas, of her father Rengal and her mother Dorea. Kristiana had fled, coming to this strange corner of the universe, fleeing from the thing that had threatened their survival.

The anger grew in her, the generations of Atlanteans flowing through her ancient blood, calling her again to protect her people. Kristiana took hold of the anger, concentrating upon it, directing it as it moved through her. Now her anger focused, a single point of energy growing within her. She let go of it, directing it into the rock she stood upon; meeting with the energy that surged up to meet it. The energy of the core of the planet. The power of the waters flowing beneath her, cascading, spiralling through million-year-old ducts, swirling, surging up and into her. Her anger was now controlled, giving it direction, focus, substance. Never before had she attempted to call upon such forces and she knew that this would be the last time she would know power.

She was conscious of Traun beside her and a feeling of affection touched her. The energy which was his being was now controlled by her and their bodies grew together, a coupling of energy which gave her the strength of many. She knew Traun now. She knew how much he cared for her and for their people. And his loyalty was as vast as the power she controlled.

Now, the forces beneath her, long dormant, lay within, waiting for her. The glistening dome which now surrounded them glowed white-hot, and she knew that their physical bodies, no longer able to withstand the energy, had ceased to function. Only her vast intellect and her life-force kept them whole.

Kristiana's mind now ranged upward, away from the surface of the planet. She felt, rather than saw, the terror that confronted them. Even with the energy at her disposal, she knew that she could not destroy the forces of Borgnoff. It had the power of an entire sun at Its disposal. What she could do was to stop It, however briefly.

In what was left of her consciousness, she thought again of Earth, of the greatness of Midreas, of the monument to Psorsis, of the history of the Atlanteans. Her last thought, then, was for humanity, hiding, hoping, and she knew that she must stop Borgnoff in order that they should survive.

She focused the energy on the thing that was above them. Her mind gave way to a thought, and with the intellect that was Traun, she released the energy, letting it move, now, out. Up. Away from its source. Up to face the vast force of energy that confronted them.

Jonathan watched the longest flash and was almost blinded. Barnabus and Cathy covered their eyes, not believing what they saw. A mile away, in the centre of what was left of the city, a great surge of energy shot up from the core of the planet, pounding its way through the atmosphere, striking at the heart of the sun that descended upon them.

"Jonathan, for God's sake, close the door!" Barnabus hurried away, back towards the rear of the chamber. Jonathan slammed the door on the terror that moved towards them. "Come on, quickly!"

"What was that?" Jonathan staggered back into the centre of

the room. Cathy and Barnabus knelt by the computer.

Quickly, the teacher placed a microprocessor into a recess. He turned, meeting the boy's frightened eyes. "My guess is that it was Kristiana. Something tells me she's trying to buy us a little time."

"With what?"

The scholar shook his head. "You never really understood her, Jonathan. She has had thousands of years to hone her intellect. What you saw was a mastery of control. I believe that she loosed a fraction of the planet's natural power at our nemesis." He looked at the page out of the scroll, reading the equations once again. He began keying them into the computer. "God knows if I'm right or not. If I'm incorrect, Kristiana will have sacrificed herself in vain. And Traun, too, I think. So let's hope that I'm right."

He finished the data entry and punched the input key. The laptop ran back through its programme and proceeded to complete the instruction.

Cathy looked at her teacher. "I take it that you're burning a programme into the microprocessor?"

Barnabus nodded. "That's right. This will be inserted into the circuit-board. With it we'll be able to tap into the full potential of the planet's energy. Vectoring it towards a focal point which is necessary if I'm to complete this . . . ah . . . assignment." He looked up at Jonathan. "Now, if you would be so kind, Jonathan, I'd like you and Cathy to start reassembling the scrolls. Place the box into its place in the dais first. Then transfer the pages."

"How about the broken ones?"

"Put them all in. Even pieces. I suspect that the scrolls act as something of a lens. Focusing the power beneath it and then shooting it up into the body of the operator. Now, quickly! We don't have much time."

Jonathan and Cathy did as they were instructed, first lifting the box into the recessed chamber which lay within the quartz altar, then transferring the individual pages of the scrolls into the box. As they did so, Barnabus moved quickly, now inserting the programmed microprocessor into its position, then moving the lumpy assembly of electronics equipment toward the dais.

"Have you finished with the scrolls?"

Jonathan and Cathy stood, Jonathan wiping the sweat away from his face on the black surface of the Atlantean armour that he still wore. He looked at Cathy. "Yeah, they're all in there. Even the little pieces. I only hope that we didn't throw in some dirt by mistake."

Barnabus glanced at them sharply. "I must say, I hope so, too. If you did, it will upset the properties of the scrolls. God knows that they're in bad enough condition as they are." He moved closer, studying the layout of the scrolls. "Right. Now, on Earth I was dealing only with the focal properties of the quartz. Of course, I had more equipment there, so I was able to utilise its full potential. Here, I'm dealing with a more complex entity, made so by the presence of the scrolls. Of course, I'm also working with less sophisticated electronic equipment."

Jonathan stood, staring glumly at the teacher. "Barnabus. Borgnoff is right outside. Remember? Do you mind skipping the lecture for a change?"

"Ah, yes. Right! Well, now, let's see if this works." Carefully, he lowered the electronic assembly on to the scrolls' housing. Then he connected it, feeding a series of wires in through the housing, dangling around the glass plates. He looked again, then satisfied with his work, mounted the dais. As he did, the dais began to glow, its crystalline structure radiating light.

"Now, are you ready?"

Jonathan glanced at the electronic gear. "You mean that's it?"

The teacher nodded. "Yes, Jonathan. That's it. Now, let's see if we can put the knowledge of a man named Psorsis into practical application!"

Cathy moved over, standing beside Jonathan, feeling his arm wrap tightly around her. He looked at her briefly. "If this works, I definitely want that date."

She looked back at him, her eyes glistening. "You've got it!"

Then Barnabus extended his arms, reaching out, again feeling the power entering into him. As he did so, the room darkened, and above them the twin suns of the planet rose above the horizon. Then, the room was engulfed in the intense red light of the Giant Sun, and the turgid energy which was Borgnoff.

It had them, now, and a satisfaction which It had not known for aeons swept through Its being, devouring Its senses as it did so. It had taken control of the red sun with little effort. It had merely forced Its intellect upon it, challenging the raw forces for control. Then, the entity which the Atlanteans called Borgnoff *was* the Red Giant, and now It would control the forces of the sun as It willed.

The Atlanteans had always been irritants. But their powers were only a minor irritant to a grand plan – a plan which Borgnoff had long ago fashioned.

For aeons, It had run amok in this portion of the universe, destroying any life form in its path. Destruction for destruction's sake. A statement to Its brethren on the far side of the universe. Then It had encountered the Atlanteans. They had proven much more powerful than any other culture which It had met before. The secret to that power, It now knew, rested in the scrolls which It had captured, but which were again lost. With such knowledge, It could have destroyed the Atlanteans; It could have tapped into the unlimited energy of the universe. And with that, It would have turned on those who had shunned It. It would have moved to conquer and liquidate naKuna.

Rage stirred in Borgnoff as It stared at the planet drifting helplessly through the vacuum of space. With Its intellect, It had reached out, shifting gravitational forces, moving the red sun away from its fixed orbit through the universe, moving it now towards the planet and the beings who populated it. It could wait, now, and let the universal forces take control. Wait as the gravity of the sun brought the planet closer. Wait as the enemy was swallowed into the great pulsing red heat which was the core of the giant sun. It felt victory swell within Its being. Powerful. Egocentric. Omnipotent.

In its vainglory, It did not at first detect the movement of energy below It. Sworling suddenly out of the core of the planet. Driving up. Crossing the gulf of emptiness in a moment. Striking It. Blinding It.

The entity which was Borgnoff shifted slightly, willing the power at Its disposal to drive off the energy. To neutralise it. It had never known real surprise. Not once in a thousand millenia. But now It knew surprise.

The energy confronting It was sharp. Focused. Controlled. As it whipped through the void between the two worlds, it manipulated the gravitational forces moving between them. The fall of the planet slowed, then stopped. Now, Borgnoff fought, and as It fought It met them. Intellect. Within the focus of energy whipping towards the evil. An intellect which was not one, but two. Their faces burning. Determined. Knowing. Hating. Using their minds to throw what energy was available in a last effort to defend their own kind.

It made no difference. The potential power of the intellects confronting It was no threat to a being which controlled the energy resources of a sun. Borgnoff sent out Its mind into the glowing neutrons and electrons which were a part of it. Shaping them to Its will. Borgnoff struck Its enemy again and again. Great arcs of energy lashed out, away from the red sun, striking at the core of the power which confronted It. Again and again, It lashed out, and as It did so, It felt Its ancient enemy weakening. The power within them dying. Until at last, the righteous intellects which were Kristiana and Traun collapsed inward on themselves, glowing for a moment – a final spark of bravery and glory – and then dying, leaving only the darkness of the universe, and the threat that hung there.

Borgnoff turned then, towards the defenseless planet, putting out Its mind to complete the act. It saw then. The movement in the near distance. Space wrinkling, the light of the universal centre dancing for a moment in the face of Its being. The knowledge that naKuna were here. With It. And in that moment, what humans called Borgnoff knew that It had lost.

It saw, but it had not yet decelerated completely, so it could not act. It knew, however, that what it was witnessing was the sacrifice of the few for the many. In the face of overwhelming resources, the beings who controlled the insignificant finger of ancient energy died out of love for their fellow creatures.

It understood this. Rage such as it had never known washed through its intellect. While it could not and would not destroy its brother, it would not let this madness destroy again. With the knowledge of a billion years, it moved to act.

"Hold on!" The earthquake whipped again through the monument, its force grabbing at them. Barnabus fell heavily on to the face of the dais, and for a moment the energy beneath him died. Then he was up again, his arms outstretched, attempting to control the energy which engulfed him.

"For God's sake, hurry, Barnabus!" Jonathan and Cathy lay on the floor where they'd been thrown. From there, they could see their teacher, concentrating, trying to control the powers beneath him with an untrained mind. His lined face was white, sweat dripping from his moustache. He muttered through gritted teeth, "I must wait. I must wait for the power to build!"

The dais turned white, blinding, the energy beneath it converging through the scrolls. Jonathan could look down into the bowels of the planet. From every direction, he saw water cascading towards him, swirling in great waves as the waters of the planet were brought to them, focusing the entire might of their energy on a point just below them.

Then the floor seemed to split, and he looked down beyond the waters, into the very core of the planet. This broke, moving up towards them, a red furnace from below mixing with the red light from the sun above them. Colliding with the roaring water, turning into steam, enough energy to drive the engines of all mankind for a thousand years.

They were moving, hurtling out and away from the surface. Through the heart of the Red Giant. Past the orbits of the twin suns, who would soon lose one of their children. Barnabus concentrated, drifting for a moment in the void, uncertain of his direction. Then he knew, not sure why he knew, that Kristiana herself must be directing him. Or Psorsis. Or the countless dead children of the people of Atlantis. Now the stars were cascading toward them, the whorling galaxies dancing to their timeless tune. For a moment he stopped, turning about. The stars rotated, and he looked down on the Red Giant, a small gleaming red disc.

In the glimmering of that vision, he saw it but did not understand it. The Red Giant pulsed now with an energy that he could not comprehend. Moving out. Overtaking the orbit of Atlantis. Of the planet on which he stood. Yet he felt nothing. He thought for a moment that Borgnoff had eclipsed unheard of forces, but then he noted the glimmering, the tear in the fabric of the universe, and thought that perhaps he understood.

Again he spun, searching the distant constellations. He saw it, then. The gleaming symbol of Atlantis. Placed to mark their way home. He threw his concentration out, and now they moved at speed too great to measure. The stars rushed past them, mere spider-webs of light. They traversed whole galaxies in milliseconds. And as they did so, the whorl of Atlantis grew larger. Until it filled the horizon. A golden sworl of light that symbolised refuge. And home.

Now they were upon it and Barnabus slowed. He paused here and they looked down upon the planets of their Sun, its warm light bathing the chamber in soft yellows, welcoming them – and its lost children of Atlantis – back into its comforting care.

Cathy pointed. "Earth! There!" There it was, Earth, a blue-white jewel set in an ebony sky.

Barnabus spoke, careful not to disturb his concentration. "We're not home yet. Remember that what we're seeing is merely a transmission. As if this chamber were a satellite, moving relentlessly through the universe. We won't be home until we transport the entire planet from its present position into a safe orbit around the sun."

He studied the orbital layout of the planets, thinking. They were beautiful to look at. The rich reds of Mars. The swirling hues of Jupiter. The fragile ring system of Saturn. He knew them all so well. And now he would add another to their system. A tenth planet. And he must do so with as little damage to their gravitational equilibrium as possible.

For the planet of Atlantis to live, it must remain at a distance from the sun which approximated that of the Earth. But he had to position the planet in direct solar opposition. In this way, Atlantis would receive the warmth and solar energy required for living. At the same time, and assuming that its mass was roughly the same as Earth's, it should not disturb the orbital configuration of any of the other planets significantly.

Now they were speeding towards the elliptic, pausing for a moment over Earth, gazing at the blue of its waters, the white sworling masses of its cloud formations, its lush land masses. "Home," Barnabus whispered. "And now, we bring it a sister to keep our Earth company."

The teacher moved quickly then. As they swept past the sun, he felt the dais twist. Atlantis, the equilibrium of its orbit changed with the demise of the Red Giant, shook with an earthquake. Barnabus staggered for a moment. Then he moved decisively. He rotated the vision in front of them, looking now across the sun, watching the faint white star that from this distance was Earth.

"Put your heads down!" Barnabus glanced quickly over his shoulder. Jonathan shielded Cathy with his body. "Now!" Barnabus cried. "I'm transporting now!" He reached out with his mind one last time. As he did, the power beneath him was released, filling his being with its force.

naKuna saw, instinctively understanding. The power was released, and they watched with something approaching awe as the fabric of space rippled for a moment. The planet wavered. If the entity of naKuna was human, it would have chuckled sadly, and shaken its head a little. No, they haven't got it quite right. But they are progressing. For a moment, its being focused. Additional energy moved into that flowing through Barnabus. The planet grew transparent. naKuna watched as stars appeared in the flowing depths of the planet's oceans. And as naKuna watched, the planet ceased to be. In this part of the universe, life had relinquished its tenuous grip.

naKuna knew, of course, where the occupants had taken the planet. They had been there before, and now had every reason to go again. The small yellow sun with its nine planets held a struggling society. This new life form would enter into that system. And it would have powers which would prove of interest even to naKuna.

And as for its brother? The entity sent from naKuna – the People – contemplated its decision for a moment. What had been done had been necessary. Even now, what remained of the Red Giant hurtled through the void, the warped spirit which humans called Borgnoff trapped within it confines. Soon, the dying sun would know its destination. Collapsed energy which formed a whirlpool of fantastic forces would swallow its deviant sibling, holding it there for all eternity. Now, perhaps, younger and more ambitious civilisations than its own could be left in peace to develop as they needed.

naKuna turned then to follow this new intellect. It would take its time, of course. There were many galaxies between its present point and its destination. Galaxies which teemed with life. It would spend some time, perhaps, nurturing. And when naKuna at last arrived in the planetary system of these travellers, perhaps then they would be ready for its help.

Epilogue

"Jonathan! Jonathan! Time to hit the bed." He rose wearily from the overstuffed chair, and stretched. "OK, Dad. Give me a second, will you?"

He heard some rumblings from the kitchen. "Remember, you have that maths test tomorrow. Come on. Get on up to your bedroom."

"All right. I'll see you in the morning."

He climbed the stairs wearily. It had been a tough day. He smiled at the thought. "Not as tough as a couple of days I've had recently." He laughed a little, thinking back. It had been really something. He hadn't been here at the time, of course. He had still been on Atlantis. But apparently, the media had really made something of it. The sudden appearance of a new planet in the system would, of course, give cause for alarm. For weeks, the governments of all the world powers had sat in closed session and special meetings of the United Nations lasted into the early hours. But the governments could do nothing. Even the fastest unmanned probe would take years to reach the new planet's orbit. No, they had to wait.

But that was nothing compared to the reaction at the sudden reappearance of one teacher, a pretty girl, and a wounded fellow dressed in black flexible armour. That *really* made the headlines.

It had taken almost a month to get the remnants of the Atlantean monument back in shape. And even then, they had to piece the quartz dais back together. But finally, they were able to organise transport. They had left the people of Atlantis gazing into a sun which their forefathers had known, and which they had heard of in legend. They were again protected in its gentle warmth and the Atlanteans now started to rebuild. They would not be the same, of course. Not without Kristiana and Traun. But they would find a new leader. And of course, there was still the untapped wisdom hidden in the scrolls of Psorsis.

Barnabus, of course, wanted to remain behind. He was convinced that, given time, he could unlock all of the answers contained in the undamaged sections of the scrolls. He knew, however, that he had to go back – back to his life on his home planet. So he compromised. "I'll bring only ten of the pages with me, Jonathan. That should keep me going for a few years."

The Atlanteans had seen them off. They watched as Barnabus again harnessed the power, as the three stepped through into the other, smaller chamber which their ancestors had built so many years ago. The Atlanteans would not come with them. Not yet. They were not ready. But someday, they would come back to the place of their birth, back to the land of Psorsis. And on that day, Kristiana's dream would become reality. The old race of Atlantis would mix with the blood of their ancient ancestors. And on that day, a great new life would be breathed back into the human race. Surely this had been worth the destruction of their leaders. Their deaths had rescued the lost scrolls of Psorsis.

Jonathan thought back. The lost scrolls, he thought. Lost and now found. Much as the Atlantean people – once thought lost to the rest of humanity – had now been found again.

Jonathan reached the top of the stairs and entered his bedroom. He stopped at the window, gazing out over the horizon. A gentle breeze blew into his room, soft twilight on his face. Jonathan stood and looked out over the small hills, at a group of storm clouds that grew high into the sky. Beyond the hills lay Newgrange. Still functioning, though Barnabus had not yet told the authorities. No, Barnabus had said, the Atlanteans were not yet ready for a wholesale invasion from their motherland. Nor were people from Earth ready to visit other parts of the universe. For now, Barnabus intended to keep the secret of Newgrange to himself. And he asked Jonathan and Cathy to keep the promise, too.

Lightning flashed. Jonathan stared at the storm clouds for a moment. Then relaxed, reassuring himself. "It isn't Borgnoff," he whispered to himself. No, that great nemesis was not here. Not yet, anyway. But some day . . . some day. It might come searching. And then he would have to face It again.

But not now. No. For now, he would go to bed. Turn off the light. Get ready for that maths test. His book lay propped on the pillow. He smiled briefly. Cathy was tutoring him, now. And tomorrow night . . . they were going to the pictures. Then maybe the disco. They'd just see how things got on. After Borgnoff, anything was possible.

"Jonathan!" The voice of his father tumbled up the stairs. "Bed!"

"Some things just don't change!" Jonathan reached over and turned out the light.

Author's notes and acknowledgements

I am indebted to three books which greatly influenced my thinking, and which gave me some preliminary understanding of the majesty of the Newgrange passage grave. MJ O'Kelly, one of Ireland's most renowned archaeologists, provided a wealth of knowledge in his highly informative book, *Early Ireland* (Cambridge University Press, 1989). His wife, Claire O'Kelly, an eminent archaeologist in her own right, supplemented my thinking in her booklet, "Concise Guide to Newgrange," (Claire O'Kelly, 1991).

While I borrowed many factual accounts of the structure of Newgrange, and its supposed construction, I have also altered those accounts where it helped the reader to more clearly understand the complex undertaking which megalithic man undertook when building Newgrange. For an authoritative understanding of the Newgrange monument, I refer the reader to the O'Kellys' work.

I am also indebted to PA Ó Síocháin and his book *Ireland. A Journey into Lost Time*. This highly interesting and entertaining work provided me with the link between the Atlantean culture and the people who built Newgrange. This proved to be a cornerstone in my thinking and greatly enriched my creative approach when writing *The Lost Scrolls of Newgrange*.

Then, too, there are the many, many people who encouraged me as I sought to realise the personal dream of publishing this first novel. My editor, Nicole Jussek, pushed and prodded the original rough manuscript into a much more polished story. By making me be hard on myself, I believe she honed this into a more enjoyable read. The fact that she is a fellow UCLA graduate has not biased this opinion. My other editors, Jo O'Donoghue and Sean McMahon, put up with the assorted frenzied phone calls from this first-time author, and to them I give grateful thanks. Copy editor Anne O'Neill – a new found friend – transformed a rough manuscript through her hard work. As with all of the people who influenced this book, her compassion helped to mould *The Lost Scrolls of Newgrange* into a better work.

My thanks also to the people at Ireland's Office of Public Works, and particularly to the staff manning the Newgrange exhibit for allowing me access to the monument at any time.

My wife, Bernadette, and my children, Kristin, Cathy and Jonathan, have proven more than an inspiration to me. They are the focus of my love and affection.

My parents, Bill and Mary, and my sister, Cindy, though thousands of miles away, were often in my thoughts as I wrote this. From them, I gained not only life and love, but an education for which I will be always grateful.

My teacher and mentor, Ron Raben, gave me the rough tools of language and thought. And while life has helped to hone these further, his initial encouragement to reach for the seemingly unobtainable has always stayed with me.

And finally, there is one man who helped me to look towards the stars, even though I have never met him. In 1969, in a theatre in Arlington Heights, Illinois, a youngster watched in awe as a giant monolith moved silently through the darkness of Jupiter's space. On that day, something sparked within him. In grateful thanks, then, to Mr Arthur C Clarke, the world's most renowned science fiction writer, and for the gift of curiosity which he gave to one small, unknown boy.

Navan, County Meath, Ireland.
Spring, 1994.

Also by Poolbeg

The Brod of Bres Trilogy by Mary Regan

The Pit of the Hell Hag
The Spirit of the Foyle
The Red Stone of the Curses

Three books comprising a fantasy trilogy which trace the adventures of Aileen Kennedy and Robin Drake. Both children are lonely outcasts, bullied mercilessly at school. Their worlds are shattered by family upheavals and they are unable to settle happily into their new lives. Perhaps because of this they are drawn into the Otherworld and are vulnerable to the wiles of the Morriagan – the Shapshifter. The courage and quick thinking they display when in danger help them to solve difficulties in their own world.

An exciting trilogy based on the mythology of the Invasions when the Tuatha De Danaan came to Ireland and became locked in battle with Fomar.

Also by Poolbeg

Distant Voices

by

Maeve friel

This voice, this Harald, was haunting her dreams, speaking to her in his strange accent, drawing her into another life . . . She began to feel as if he had burrowed beneath her skin and was using her sleep to spin dreams thronged with strange men from long ago, their distant voices straining to be heard.

Each night Ellie is haunted by a mysterious figure who spins stories of sea voyages, exile and death while she sleeps. His appeal to Ellie, *"Only you will know where to find me"* leads her to crossing the border from Derry into Donegal where she makes a startling discovery on a lonely headland.

Set in the North-west of Ireland, Maeve Friel's book is a powerful and unusual evocation of the Viking Era.

"Friel's language and dialogue are not unlike Anne Fine's: they are loaded with character implications."

Children's Books Ireland